THE REDISCOVERY OF TOBACCO

SMOKING, VAPING, AND THE CREATIVE DESTRUCTION OF THE CIGARETTE

JACOB GRIER

Cover illustration by Andrew Bohrer.

ISBN:

Hardcover: 978-1-7340125-0-7

Paperback: 978-1-7340125-1-4

E-Book: 978-1-7340125-2-1

www.jacobgrier.com

❀ Created with Vellum

CONTENTS

INTRODUCTION

Audite et alteram partem. [Listen even to the other side.]
— Inscription on the old city hall in Gouda, Netherlands[1]

IN THE LATE 1980s, the United States began extinguishing smoking on airplanes. "Smoking or non?" became a standard question at restaurants, then disappeared when outright bans took the smoking option off the table altogether. The reach of these prohibitions has extended ever since: to the bar, the restaurant patio, the college campus, the beach, the golf course, the park, the bus stop, the sidewalk, even to the home. More than at any time in modern history, today's nonsmokers can go about their lives without being subjected to smokers' fumes.

Few people, myself included, wish to turn the clock back entirely. Though I'm too young to remember smoking on airplanes, it strikes me as guaranteed to make flying unpleasant. As both an employee and patron of bars and restaurants, I'm happy that most of them are now smoke-free. I'm glad that the residents of my apartment building sign lease agreements forbidding indoor smoking, preventing the odor of cigarettes from permeating our living spaces. In hindsight, the extent to which smokers were once permitted to impose their preference onto everyone else appears astonishing.

The banishment of smokers from social spaces has, however, made it almost impossible to contemplate that tobacco deserves any tolerance. Smoking has become a low-status activity. Less than a fifth of Americans currently smoke and the habit lingers mostly among those with less education and lower incomes. Tobacco use is viewed as pure vice and the smoker as a helpless addict, deserving only pity or scorn.

I write from experience on this, having been indoctrinated into holding strongly anti-tobacco views myself. As a child, I pestered smoking cousins to quit before the habit killed them. I bought completely into the view that tobacco is lethal and gross and made it all the way through college without taking so much as a single experimental puff from a cigarette – a rare feat in the philosophy department. My negative perspective on tobacco was unchallenged until I began working in the hospitality industry in one of the first high-quality coffee shops to open in Arlington, Virginia. One of my regulars there, a fitness instructor with an appreciation for well-made espresso and an intimidatingly broad knowledge of food and drink, was also, confusingly to my mind, an avid cigar smoker. On Sunday afternoons he would often step outside with his coffee to light one up. Why, I wondered, would someone who had such great taste and a career in physical fitness risk his palate and his health on those fat stogies? The contradiction perplexed me.[2]

Until, one day, he invited me to try one. I was skeptical, but he talked about his cigars in much the same way that I talked about my coffee. The varietal of the plant and origin of the leaf mattered, with tobacco from Nicaragua tasting differently than tobacco from Brazil or Cameroon. The shade of the cigar wrapper, from light claro to dark oscuro, mirrored the roasting spectrum of coffee beans. He spoke as if hand-rolled cigars made of pure leaf were as far removed from mass-market cigarettes as specialty coffee is from a can of Folgers, suggesting that cigars could be every bit as rewarding as the drink with which I was already enamored.

He was right. Although smoking my first cigar was an unfamiliar experience, I took to it quickly. I remember starting out with a light, approachable Romeo y Julieta and moving on to darker cigars like the imposing Partagas Black. With my friend guiding me through the humidor at the local tobacconist, his Sunday ritual soon became my own. For the next few years we met every weekend to drink coffee, smoke cigars, and read books — out on the patio in good weather, in the backroom of a nearby gastropub when it was raining or cold. The experience was enriching both for the cigar smoke itself and for the thoughtful conversations it reliably drew forth. Today I look back on those Sunday afternoons as some of the happiest moments of my time in Virginia.

Those who wish to eliminate smoking from the world fail to imagine tobacco as a craft product deserving of appreciation and as a wonderful complement to life's enjoyments. After decades of commodification, consumers have discovered better wine, beer, coffee, cocktails, meat, chocolate, and produce. Specialty stores, farmers markets, diverse restaurants, and craft breweries have made this the most rewarding time ever to be a lover of food and drink in the United States. Yet it's one of the worst times to be a smoker. Tastemakers and lawmakers alike ignore the desires of smokers and their reasons for keeping up the practice. The proliferation of smoking bans makes it harder than ever to find a place to light up; tax hikes make it increasingly expensive; adoption agencies and employers discriminate against smokers; government regulations favor Big Tobacco over small producers and deadly cigarettes over safer alternatives. Though Philip Morris remains ever profitable, the quality side of the tobacco market is threatened with destruction by the Food and Drug Administration. To those of us who do take pleasure in smoking, this presents a puzzle: How did attitudes toward tobacco get so completely backwards when so many other products are getting so much better?

* * *

AT THE SAME TIME THAT I WAS DISCOVERING THE PLEASURES OF tobacco in Arlington, neighboring Washington, DC, was in the process of passing legislation to ban smoking in bars and restaurants. Though I worked primarily in the service industry, I was also active in various libertarian organizations in the area. Many of my friends in that movement, regardless of their own smoking status, vehemently opposed the measure. A few of them formed Ban the Ban, an organization whose members rallied the opposition with t-shirts and stickers bearing slogans like "Smoking is Healthier than Fascism."

I sided with Ban the Ban for straightforward libertarian reasons. I believed it was the right of private business owners, employees, and customers to make their own choices about whether to allow smoking. If patrons didn't like it, they could take their business elsewhere. Even if secondhand smoke was as harmful as anti-smoking activists claimed — a question I hadn't yet explored — in a liberal society people should be free to make their own bad decisions. That, for me, was enough to settle the issue.

For the Washington, D.C. city council, and many other

lawmakers nationwide, that liberty-focused argument was not compelling. Bans spread all over the country, eventually even to tobacco-friendly Virginia where my friend and I enjoyed our Sunday afternoon cigars. As of this writing, forty-three states and more than 22,000 municipalities have enacted bans in hospitality spaces.[3] To secure places for smokers to light up in peace, I realized, a defense of tobacco itself is needed, one that challenges the perception that smoking is pure vice. This set me on a course of researching and writing about tobacco for more than a decade, covering the topic for *The Atlantic, Slate, Reason,* and other publications.

I found that the landscape of smoking research had shifted considerably since the days when bold epidemiologists took on deceitful tobacco companies to conclusively prove that cigarettes were causing an epidemic of lung cancer. When the companies settled lawsuits with state governments in 1998, they agreed to shut down industry-funded institutes that provided pro-smoking talking points and to funnel tobacco money to anti-smoking researchers and advocacy groups. While this was certainly a positive development in some respects, anti-smoking activists lost an incentive for doing rigorous science when they de-fanged their long-time adversaries. They found themselves free to say anything they wanted without fear of contradiction.

And say anything they did. The more I researched the epidemiology of secondhand smoke, the more I realized how often the claims of anti-smoking activists were wildly exaggerated. Given what we know about the dangers of firsthand smoke, it's sensible to suspect that secondhand smoke poses some danger, too. But determining exactly how dangerous it is, and at what levels of exposure, has proven to be difficult. Anti-smoking researchers take advantage of this ambiguity to elide any doubts. They cherry-pick data, attack contrary evidence, and magnify tiny risks. Their actions reveal a willingness to sacrifice quality science for the supposedly greater goods of stigmatizing smoking and imposing new restrictions.

One leading researcher, for example, claimed that a smoking ban in the small city of Helena, Montana, had slashed local heart attacks by nearly 60% in just six months.[4] Though wildly implausible, this finding was reported uncritically everywhere from CBS to the *New York Times* op/ed page. Dubbed the "Helena Miracle" by critics, it has, like all miracles, proved immune to replication on a larger scale. Subsequent research has completely debunked the idea that simply banning smoking in bars and restaurants can achieve such remarkable results. Yet the assertion that bans drastically reduce heart attacks continues to justify increasingly restrictive prohibitions that push smokers ever further to the fringes of society, leaving them with progressively fewer places to go.

Not content with demonizing secondhand smoke, researchers also turned their attention to "thirdhand smoke," a term for the residue left behind on clothing and other surfaces when someone lights up nearby. For the past decade, thirdhand smoke has featured in countless news stories portraying smokers as objects of revulsion. "Smokers themselves are also contaminated... smokers actually emit toxins," one researcher explained to *Scientific American*.[5] In the words of another, smokers are "mobile tobacco contamination packages."[6] Despite a lack of evidence that thirdhand smoke is a substantial health concern for actual living humans, the concept has been used to stigmatize not just smoking, but smokers themselves, rendering their mere existence in social spaces an unhygienic intrusion.

Anti-smoking ideology now tragically extends to products

that emit no smoke at all. A rapidly accumulating body of evidence suggests that products such as electronic cigarettes are far less dangerous than combustible tobacco and that they are helping smokers quit their destructive habit. Instead of embracing these advances, however, anti-smoking groups feed the public a fear-driven narrative that associates vaping with cancer, heart disease, seizures, popcorn lung, exploding devices, dangerous chemicals, and addiction to narcotics. The factual basis for these claims is often tenuous at best. The abstinence-only demands of traditional tobacco control are having a corrosive effect on research into harm reduction, repeating the excesses of the debate over smoking bans and often originating from the same biased sources.

Journalists routinely rely on experts to interpret scientific results, but good journalists must also take the motivations of their sources into account. Years of self-serving manipulation by Big Tobacco accustomed reporters to a simple dynamic: Anything the pro-smoking side claimed was presumed to be a self-serving lie, while anti-smokers were on the side of truth and public health. The press has, with few exceptions, failed to turn a skeptical eye on anti-smoking activism, which today is guided as much by ideology as it is by science. As a result, journalists, politicians, and the public hold beliefs about tobacco, secondhand smoke, and electronic cigarettes that are contradicted by the best and most up-to-date scientific research, and restrictions go far beyond what can be justified by any reasonable interpretation of the evidence. Potentially life-saving products are burdened by excessive bureaucracy, targeted with legal prohibitions, and subjected to moral panic.

The aim of this book is to sort truth from ideology and give tobacco its proper due, beginning with a look at Europeans' first encounters with the plant — a time when smoking was strange and unknown outside of the Americas, long before the twentieth century rise of Big Tobacco and the inescapable ubiquity of the cigarette. It ends with a look at the innovative products that are revolutionizing the market for nicotine once again. In contrast to most contemporary writing on tobacco, this book looks beyond the public health framing that views smoking as a purely medical problem and denies smokers' agency and dignity. I take a longer and wider view, drawing on insights from history, sociology, anthropology, epidemiology, economics, law, and political philosophy to provide a more fully developed perspective on smoking and the anti-smoking movement. My approach values both health and liberty, and while acknowledging the real dangers of smoking, it unapologetically refuses to allow the former to run roughshod over the latter.

* * *

AN OFTEN-REPEATED ANECDOTE EXPRESSES HOW NOVEL THE habit of pipe smoking appeared when it first arrived in England. It usually features Sir Walter Raleigh, though it is also attributed to Richard Tarlton, an actor and clown of the era. Which of the two hardly matters, for the story is almost certainly fictional.

According to the tale, a servant or a couple of passersby see Raleigh or Tarlton exhaling smoke after taking a drag from a pipe. Having never witnessed someone smoking before, they leap to the obvious conclusion: The smoker must be on fire! To save his life they douse the flames with a glass of wine or ale. As the version in *Tarltons Jests* has it, two men, "neuer seeing the like, wondreth at it: and seeing the vapour come out of Tarltons nose cryed out, Fire, fire, and threw a cup of Wine in Tarltons face."[7]

The story is an apt metaphor for our fraught relationship with tobacco. Raleigh or Tarlton, enjoying pipe tobacco for its pleasurable effects, could not have foreseen the tremendous toll in human lives the crop would take centuries later when traditional pipes gave way to modern cigarettes. The naive passersby, splashing wine in the smoker's face in the false belief that they were doing him a favor, were equally blind to the joys tobacco offers.

Today the dangers of tobacco are well known and the anti-smoking movement, oblivious to the leaf's redeeming virtues, has acquired some very large tankards of wine with which to drown its use. But the proper path lies somewhere between ignorant pleasure and outright prohibition — a path this book will map in the pages to follow.

FROM NEW WORLD TO OLD

How could I know that beyond the tastes of this world
There would be yet another worth tasting?
— Cao Xibao[1]

IT'S difficult to imagine Italian cuisine without tomatoes, French pastries without vanilla and chocolate, or Southeast Asian curries without the fire of chili peppers. Yet prior to Christopher Columbus's arrival in the New World, these and many other foods were unknown outside of the Americas. The age of European exploration and colonization of the western continents ushered in an exchange of indigenous plants and animals that were rapidly and eagerly adopted across the globe, becoming such an integral part of the culinary landscape that it's easy to forget that they were once exotic and new. These transformative crops included cashews, corn, peanuts, avocados, lima beans, potatoes, and pineapples.[2]

And tobacco.

When Columbus and his crew first made landfall in the

Bahamas, tobacco and the act of smoking were as foreign to them as the turf they walked on. So was the local culture; Columbus believed he'd arrived in Asia, as per his original plan. He went ashore with gifts of beads and red hats. The natives requited with gifts of their own, including dried leaves. The leaves were tobacco, and although Columbus soon discerned that they were valued by the natives, no one among the crew had any idea what to do with them.[3]

Confusing first encounters with tobacco were not unusual for Europeans. Florentine explorer Giovanni da Verrazzano and his crew were party to a nearly fatal misunderstanding in Arcadia, the coast of present-day North Carolina. Verrazzano recounted an incident in which they came across "a man who came to the shore to see what [manner of men] we were... He was handsome, naked, his hair fastened in a knot, and of an olive color." The man gestured toward them with "a burning stick, as if to offer us fire." This was plausibly a tobacco pipe and the gesture a friendly offer of greeting. Verrazzano, however, read the intention as hostile and his crew responded by firing a warning musket shot at the man, "who trembled all over with fright."[4]

In hindsight, perhaps Verrazzano had the right idea. Much illness and death would have been prevented if Europeans had refused all offers of tobacco. But this state of innocence was not to last. Eventually Columbus's crew and all the world would be seduced by the plant's allure. "That the lungs had a dual function — could be used for stimulation in addition to respiration — is one of the American continent's most significant contributions to civilization," writes Iain Gately in his history *Tobacco*.[5] Though Europeans had inhaled the smoke of other herbs before, it's hard to disagree with his assessment.

Today, cigarettes are mundane, sold in packs of twenty in

every convenience store, each one mass-manufactured by machine to be perfectly identical to the one before it. Discarded butts litter sidewalks, doorways, and beaches. Huddled smokers foul the air at the entrances of buildings and a stale aroma lingers on their clothing, rudely announcing itself in smoke-free spaces. Jaded by repeated encounters, it's difficult to see tobacco with fresh eyes, or smell it with a fresh nose, the way a European explorer or Chinese emperor may have beheld a bundle of fragrant leaves from the New World centuries ago. A change in perspective is required. To fully understand tobacco use in modern times, we must first go back to the beginning, or as near as we can find it.

TOBACCO IN THE AMERICAS

Both varieties of tobacco commonly used for smoking, *Nicotiana rustica* and *Nicotiana tabacum*, are native to the Americas and would have been noticed by the first human inhabitants of South and Central America. By sometime between 5,000 and 3,000 BC, Amerindians were cultivating the plant in the Andes regions of present-day Peru and Ecuador. The Mayas, Incas, and Aztecs all enjoyed its use, and the plant spread far throughout the Americas well before the arrival of Europeans.[6]

How tobacco was first consumed is a matter of speculation. It may have been chewed. Perhaps it was taken by snuffing, the inhalation of finely ground dried tobacco leaves straight up the nasal passages. Or maybe its distinct aroma was noticed when leaves were accidentally set alight. We do know that the variety of ways early Americans used tobacco stands in stark contrast to the ubiquity of commodified cigarettes today. In addition to smoking, chewing, and snuffing, they steeped it into liquid like a tea, rubbed it onto skin or exhaled its smoke onto the sick for healing purposes, and took it as an enema.[7] (This last practice, thankfully, never much caught on as tobacco spread around the globe.)

Amerindian uses of tobacco extended far beyond the recreational. The simplest form of consumption, chewing on the leaves, offered useful analgesic qualities. A person suffering from a toothache, for example, could find relief by packing leaves around the infected tooth.[8] The appetite-suppressing effect of tobacco, familiar to many former smokers who find themselves wider in the waist after quitting, would have also been useful for hard-laboring people with limited resources. Parcels of tobacco could be kept under the lip for gradual absorption, keeping the user alert and warding off pangs of hunger, in much the same way that coca leaves are still used in the Andes.[9]

Snuffing was extremely common and early insufflators — hollow reeds or bones that delivered tobacco powder to the nostril — have been found in abundance. With these tools a user could snort pulverized, dried tobacco leaves, possibly mixed with coca or other herbs. Another form of convenient tobacco use was "tobacco licking." In this method, tobacco tea was boiled down into a jelly, sometimes with alkaline salts added or thickened with manioc starch, then smeared onto the gums for oral absorption.[10]

More extreme methods of tobacco consumption found their way into religious rituals. In small doses, nicotine acts as a mild stimulant. At higher doses it can have dramatic effects on the body, inducing hallucinations and trances, and even causing death. These effects of tobacco, perhaps supplemented by other mind-altering drugs, were an integral part of shamanic rituals that often served an allegedly medicinal purpose. In some cases, the cure may have been more unpleasant than the disease. Francis Robicsek, a physician and scholar of Mesoamerican culture, describes the Chorti Mayan *ah huht*, or "spitter,":[11]

> The *ah huht* is called to cure seizures, ward off the evil eye or treat 'strong blood', especially in children, which makes him something of a paediatric shaman. The *ah huht* chews different herbs, such as rue, sage, and artemisia, but most often tobacco, and spits it onto the patient from head to toe. If the illness is especially severe, he sprays his saliva-mixed tobacco in the form of a cross from head to crotch and shoulder-to-shoulder. This treatment is repeated until the patient gets well or dies.

Robicsek describes a similar ritual among Amazonian Indians in which a healer drinks *natema*, a combination of tobacco juice and an herbal extract called *piripiri*. After taking this potion, the healer is purportedly able to see into the patient's body. To effect healing, he then regurgitates all over the patient.[12] If nothing else, treatments such as these provide an incentive for the patient to get better.

By the time Europeans arrived in the Americas, tobacco use had taken recognizably modern forms. Early versions of cigars have been documented, consisting of filler, binder, and wrapper, similar to — though considerably longer than — those sold in stores today. There were also early versions of cigarettes. Some used a corn-leaf wrapper instead of paper, a method that is still employed in Mesoamerica. Other cigarettes were made by stuffing short lengths of reed or cane with powdered tobacco.[13] In Panama, Europeans reported use of an extraordinarily long cigar used in reverse of the typical fashion, with one person blowing air through the smoldering end to expel smoke into the waiting mouths of others.[14]

As tobacco spread northward, the diversity of uses appears to have tapered off somewhat in favor of simply smoking it, particularly via pipes. Pipe smoking was nearly universal among North American Indians. The pipes ranged from large and heavy, useful only for communal purposes, to small, portable pipes carried by individuals, especially men. When a man died, his pipe was often buried with him.[15]

As in Central and South America, tobacco use in North America was frequently suffused with religious meaning. Smoking a pipe was a form of meditation and communication with gods and spirits, tobacco played a central role in many creation myths, and offerings of tobacco were made at times of harvest. Pipes were important for fostering communication between tribes, with the calumet ceremony securing peaceful trade. Even in tribes primarily devoted to hunting and gathering, the importance of tobacco often warranted special cultivation.[16]

TOBACCO TAKES OVER THE WORLD

Though it took them a while, Columbus and his crew did eventually figure out that tobacco leaves were meant for smoking. Interpreter Luis de Torres and sailor Rodrigo de Jerez were sent on a diplomatic expedition to the interior of Cuba. Accompanied by two natives, they made their way inland with beads and other items to barter for food. They also carried royal letters of introduction intended for the Great Khan, emperor of China. Unsurprisingly, they failed to find him in the Caribbean.[17] Torres and Jerez did, however, come across natives smoking tobacco, earning the distinction of becoming the first Europeans recorded to try it for themselves. As recounted in Bartolome de las Casas's *History of the Indies*:

These two Spaniards met many people on the way going back and forth to their villages, men and women, and the men always carried a firebrand in their hand and certain plants to take their smokes, which are some dried plants put into a certain leaf, dried, too, in the shape of a *mosquete* or squib made of paper... and they light it at one end and at the other they suck or chew or draw in with their breath that smoke with which their flesh is benumbed and, so to speak, it intoxicates them, and in this way they say they do not feel fatique. These *mosquetes*, or whatever we shall call them, they call *tabacos*.[18]

Tobacco's role as a stimulant is well known. Its intoxicating effects are largely forgotten today, although smokers who have absorbed too much nicotine on an empty stomach may be regretfully familiar. Las Casas also picked up on a third characteristic of tobacco: the difficulty of quitting its use. "I have known Spaniards in this island of Hispaniola who were wont to take [tobacco], and being reproved for it and told that it was a vice, they replied that it was not in their power to stop taking [it]," he wrote.[19]

Further north, the French explorer Jacques Cartier encountered tobacco among Native Americans along the St. Lawrence River. He also noted the importance of the herb and its ubiquitous presence:[20]

They also possess a herb which they pile up in great heaps during the winter, which they hold in great estimation, the men alone use it as follows: they dry it in the sun and carry it around in a little animal-skin pouch around their necks, together with a stone or horn funnel, then apply a coal to it and suck on the other end, so that their whole body is filled with smoke, so much so that it comes out of their mouth and nostrils as if from a chimney; they said it that it keeps them healthy and warm.

The appeal was lost on Cartier. "We tried out the aforementioned smoke, and having drawn it into our mouths felt that we had put ground pepper there, so hot it was." From these early descriptions, the appeal of smoking would have been unfathomable to continental Europeans.

Few suffered from that incomprehension more than Rodrigo de Jerez. Both he and Torres picked up the habit while on their expedition with Columbus. Torres stayed behind on Cuba and spent the rest of his life on the island, while Jerez returned to Ayamonte, Spain, where he introduced smoking. This caught the attention of the Spanish Inquisition, which imprisoned him for the allegedly ungodly practice.[21]

Despite this harsh reception, tobacco had promoters in Spain, too. Twentieth century tobacco propagandists could not hold a candle to Nicolas Monardes, a Spanish physician who believed that tobacco could cure just about anything. In *Joyful News Out of the Newfound World*, published in 1565, he sang its praises as a treatment for headache, stomach ache, pains of the chest, cramps, constipation, worms, swellings, toothaches, venom from poison-tipped arrows, and wounds and sores of all kinds. For many of these treatments, tobacco was not smoked, chewed, or inhaled, but rather applied as an external poultice. Monardes describes stamping the herb in a mortar along with a few drops of vinegar and then applying this mixture to a wound, which the tobacco leaves would reportedly heal.[22]

Reports of tobacco's miraculous medicinal virtues helped popularize its use despite the satanic associations of smoking it. In Spain and Portugal, it was cultivated at court under the supervision of physicians. One of them, Jean Nicot of Lisbon, credited tobacco for curing his cook of illness. Nicot sent tobacco plants and seeds to Catherine de' Medici, Queen of France, with instructions to employ the leaves medicinally as a poultice or snuff. The queen believed it cured her migraines and tobacco rapidly caught on at court. In one of history's great ironies, perfectly healthy courtiers began snuffing tobacco in the belief that it prevented cancer. Before long they were taking it habitually. Thus, it's appropriate that when scientists in the 1800s isolated the addictive alkaloid in tobacco, they named it "nicotine" in honor of its early advocate.[23]

Two aspects of tobacco's adoption in mainland Europe are especially noteworthy. One was the form of use. Despite their initial introduction to cigars, or at least something like them, early continental tobacco users tended to use poultices or snuff. The second was their motivation: Tobacco was believed to be medicinal and it wasn't immediately adopted just for pleasure, although allegedly medicinal uses helped justify the latter.

In England, too, interest in tobacco was partially motivated by the plant's medicinal qualities, but the English were also less inclined to associate smoking with the Devil and more open to adopting it for pleasure. They smoked leisurely, turned on to the practice by sailors and explorers bringing it back from the New World. Sir John Hawkins, Sir Francis Drake, and Sir Walter Raleigh all encountered tobacco on their adventures, and Raleigh in particular imbued smoking with virility and adventure. Pipes were adopted at court, with Queen Elizabeth I herself partaking.[24]

"Drinking tobacco," as the practice was then called, was rapidly integrated into English social life.[25] Smoking dens, or "tabagies," provided small clay pipes for their clientele. As smoking became a mark of fashion, new rituals and paraphernalia attached to the habit. Pipes and tobacco boxes became more elaborate; tricks such as lighting tobacco with a coal attached to a sword or blowing a perfect smoke ring became gentlemanly talents. Aficionados of pipes became known as "reeking gallants" for their showy extravagance and, obviously, their smell.[26] Tobacco spread through all social classes and into rural England, with the number of pipe makers increasing from fewer than ten in the early 1600s to more than sixty by the century's end. Consumption exceeded two pounds per capita by 1700.[27]

As in the Americas, tobacco was employed to suppress appetite when food was unobtainable. As a verse from 1611 had it:

> Whenas my purse cannot afford my stomach flesh
>   or beer,
> I sup with smoke, and feed as well and fat as one
>   can wish; […]
> Much victuals serve for gluttony to fatten men
>   like swine,
> But he's a frugal man indeed that with a leaf can
>   dine,
> And needs no napkins for his hands, his fingers'
>   ends to wipe,
> But keeps his kitchen in a box, and roast meat in a
>   pipe.[28]

Tobacco's rise in England was not without detractors and the extravagant claims made on its behalf provided fertile ground for parody.[29] King James I got in on the act, waging rhetorical war on tobacco's adherents in his 1604 treatise *A Counterblaste to Tobacco*, arguably the most famous anti-smoking tract ever written. He mocked the paradoxical effects tobacco was claimed to have on the body:

> It makes a man sober that was drunk. It refreshes a weary man, yet makes a man hungry. Being taken when they goe to bed, it makes one sleepe soundly, and yet being taken when a man is sleepie and drowsie, it will, as they say, awake his braine, and quicken his understanding.[30]

It must be admitted that King James had a point. Yet he did much more than tear down excessive medical claims. Much like modern drug warriors who campaigned for laws against marijuana and cocaine by associating them with racial outgroups, James couched his opposition to tobacco in cultural purity, lamenting that civilized Englishmen would take up the customs of supposedly inferior native Americans:

> And now good Countrey men let us (I pray you) consider, what honour or policie can moove us to imitate the barbarous and beastly maners of the wilde, godlesse, and slavish Indians, especially in so vile and stinking a custome? Shall wee that disdaine to imitate the maners of our neighbour France (having the stile of the first Christian Kingdom) and that cannot endure the spirit of the Spaniards... shall we, I say, without blushing, abase our selves so farre, as to imitate these beastly *Indians*, slaves to the *Spaniards*, refuse to the world, and as yet aliens from the holy Covenant of God? Why doe we not as well imitate them in walking naked as they doe? in preferring glasses, feathers, and such toyes, to golde and precious stones, as they do? yea why do we not denie God and adore the Devill, as they doe?

Why, asked the king, would any self-respecting Englishman not be ashamed to partake of such a habit? "A custome loth-some to the eye, hatefull to the Nose, harmefull to the braine, dangerous to the Lungs, and in the blacke stinking fume thereof, neerest resembling the horrible Stigian smoke of the pit that is bottomelesse." Let it not be said that King James did not have a way with words! Yet words have always been of limited use against the lure of tobacco, as many Surgeons General can ruefully attest. The *Counterblaste* was taken no more seriously than the exaggerated claims of tobacco's most ardent supporters. Unable to persuade smokers to give up their habit, James embraced profit over prohibition. He raised tobacco taxes and established a royal monopoly on tobacco imports.[31]

The Dutch picked up their pipe habit from the English and before long the Dutchman and his pipe were inseparable. "The smell of the Dutch Republic was the smell of tobacco," writes historian Simon Schama in *The Embarrassment of Riches*, his exploration of the Dutch Golden Age. The Dutch were noto-rious imbibers, too, which led one contemporary to remark that with their constant drinking and smoking, the Dutch were practically distilling themselves.[32] Just as they did with liqueurs and spirits, Dutch merchants took advantage of the spice trade flowing through Amsterdam to flavor their tobacco with "sauces" made of citrus, saffron, coriander, and other spices, a precursor to modern techniques for flavoring tobacco. By the end of the 1600s, Amsterdam tobacco works were processing about 12 million pounds of tobacco, much of it headed north to Scandinavia and east to Russia and Turkey. Alongside tea, alco-hol, and spices, tobacco played a key role in the Dutch economic empire.[33]

By that time, tobacco's path to the rest of the world was

assured. Sailors and colonists spread tobacco wherever they ventured, influencing local customs within native cultures. In some places it was eagerly adopted. In others, it met with stiff opposition. No anti-smoker in history can top the iron-fisted Murad IV, Sultan of the Ottoman Empire from 1623 to 1640, under whose rule smoking was punishable by death. He was said to pose undercover as a smoker and beg tobacco, executing those who kindly provided it. Other rulers imposed similarly cruel penalties. Persian smokers reportedly risked having molten lead poured down their throats. In Russia, they could have their lips slit, be exiled to Siberia, suffer castration, or endure an often-fatal flogging. In Japan, they could be fined, imprisoned, and forfeit all their property.[34] Those who brought tobacco into Catholic churches risked excommunication.[35] Yet the appeal of tobacco was hard to resist. Most governments eventually tolerated it, concluding that taxing tobacco was a better policy than murdering its users.

The use of tobacco was controversial in Islamic countries, for the plant is not mentioned in the Koran. Did the absence of a specific prohibition mean that it should be allowed? Or did tobacco fall under requirements to avoid evil and foul things? Clerics could not agree.[36] Not that it mattered; smokers continued to use tobacco whether their rulers liked it or not. Clerics in Safavid Persia noted that the water pipe or hookah, called a *qalyan*, had become so thoroughly ingrained in society that the threat of execution was not enough to eliminate its use. The Persians likely picked up tobacco from the Portuguese and the hookah via Arabia and India. Early water pipes were simply constructed from coconut shells and reeds. By the early 1600s, these had evolved into the finely crafted pipes still in use today. Hookah houses became important social hubs, pairing tobacco with another novel stimulant, coffee.[37]

Indian experience with tobacco was predated by a long tradition of smoking various mixtures of plant, animal, and inorganic ingredients in accordance with Ayurvedic principles. These customs laid the groundwork for the acceptance of tobacco, which was believed to treat asthma, cough, flatulence, toothache, worms, and even scorpion bites, but also to cause intoxication, degrade eyesight, increase menstrual flow, damage the heart, and induce impotence. Routine tobacco smoking for its own sake gradually displaced smoking guided by Ayurvedic practices.[38]

No continent was impacted more profoundly and disastrously by tobacco than Africa. Water pipes and cannabis entered East Africa via Gujaratis and Arabs. In West Africa, French sailors introduced tobacco smoking in present day Senegal and Gambia. Portuguese sailors brought it to South Africa, followed by the Dutch. Use spread rapidly throughout the continent, along with beautiful, elaborately carved wooden pipes in a stunning variety of shapes and designs. Diverse smoking traditions helped build solidarity in different communities, with smoking becoming entangled with spiritual, communal, and familial meanings.[39] The disastrous impact of tobacco, however, originated from afar. When English colonists in the Chesapeake struggled to grow labor-intensive tobacco crops, they brutally addressed the problem through the importation of African slaves. Thus, tobacco was one of the crops that cemented the institution of slavery in North America.[40]

Smoking spread to Asia via the Portuguese, Spanish, and Dutch. In Japan, cigars were among a variety of imported products labeled *nanban*, a perhaps humorous allusion to a mythical primitive people living south of the country.[41] However it was pipes, not cigars, that eventually took hold among the Japanese upper classes. Though influenced by the Dutch trading settlement at Dejima Island, Japanese smoking rituals evolved in a unique direction. The *kiseru*, a long, narrow pipe, was the preferred smoking instrument, paired with a *tabako-bon* (tobacco tray) and *tabako-ire* (tobacco case). Smoking from *kiseru* became ingrained in the formal hospitality rituals of the tea ceremony[42] and featured prominently in the pleasure districts of Edo, Osaka, Kyoto, and Nagasaki.[43]

Tobacco entered China from the southeast in Fujian, where Spanish traders brought it from the Philippines, and from the northeast, where Manchus picked up pipe smoking from Koreans and Japanese. Cultivating tobacco was much more lucrative than growing grain and Fujian and Manchurian tobacco became commercially significant. This "smoke liquor" and "golden-shred inebriant" was not immediately accepted by authorities; selling tobacco carried a penalty of decapitation in Beijing, and in 1676 Emperor Kanxi banned smoking in the imperial palace. Neither prohibition lasted, and within a century China was an empire of smokers.[44]

Intriguingly, Australia was home to several species of *Nicotiana* prior to the arrival of Europeans. Aboriginal uses of tobacco as a stimulant and appetite suppressant, as an item of trade, and as a signifier of friendship and community were similar to those of Native Americans. Aboriginals cured leaves over fire and blended them into a paste which could be chewed or stored behind the ear, where nicotine would gradually enter the body through the skin.[45]

Oral use of tobacco also dominated in the United States in the 1800s. Plugs of chewing tobacco were produced by soaking cured tobacco leaves with molasses and licorice, then molding them into blocks and cutting them into rods. The consumer would whittle off a piece of this rod to form a "quid," which he would chew and tuck behind his lip. This practice of "chawing" generated a prodigious quantity of spit, which was expelled into dedicated spittoons or directly onto the ground.[46] The habit disgusted visiting Europeans, including English writer Frances Trollope, who remarked that there was no "annoyance so deeply repugnant to English feelings, as the incessant remorseless spitting of Americans."[47]

THE STAGE IS SET FOR THE CIGARETTE

In the time between Columbus's arrival in the New World and the closing of the nineteenth century, tobacco spread around the globe. From a modern perspective, what's most striking about this period is the variety of ways in which tobacco was adopted by different cultures and classes. Cigars, pipes, hookah, kiseru, chaw, and snuff took hold in different markets at different times, waxing and waning in popularity. A catalogue of the world's uses for tobacco approaching the end of the 1800s would have included the manufactured cigarette as a curious but commercially insignificant product. It was merely one of many methods of taking tobacco, gradually gaining adherents but far from being the most popular means.

In some parts of the world, this diversity of tobacco use persists: hand-rolled bidis in India, clove-scented kreteks in Indonesia, snus in Scandinavia, and water pipes and oral tobaccos in North Africa, Asia, and the Middle East.[48] Today in most of the West and in many other developed countries, however, smoking is virtually synonymous with the cigarette. Seen in historical context, the cigarette's domination of the twentieth century is a glaring anomaly, one that raises intriguing questions: Could smoking in the twenty-first century come to resemble the diversity of tobacco use in the past? Could tobacco follow the trajectory of goods like coffee and beer, rebounding from corporate consolidation to enter a new age of appreciation for quality and variety? With the nuisance of secondhand smoke virtually eliminated in the public sphere and products like e-cigarettes mitigating the dangers associated with nicotine dependence, could people begin taking renewed interest in smoking or consuming nicotine for pleasure? Is the time ripe, in short, for a rediscovery of tobacco? We'll get to those questions. But first we must examine how and why the cigarette took over the global market, with horribly lethal consequences.

FROM SMALL TOBACCO TO BIG

...the smoker of to-day cannot, watching the puffs of his cigarette float lazily upward, see in them a picturesque maiden of romantic life as its maker. In America, England, and France the romance of the cigarette is no more; the overwhelming majority of the cigarettes smoked are scientifically made by cold steel with metallic certainty...
— W. A. Penn, *The Soverane Herbe*[1]

I HAVE A PIPE SMOKING PROBLEM. By that I don't mean that I'm addicted to smoking them. I mean that I have a hard time keeping them lit. Compared to cigarettes, which ignite easily, or cigars, which continue to smolder with only an occasional puff to stoke the embers, keeping a pipe going requires care and finesse. There are more things that can go wrong with a pipe, and when they do they turn what's meant to be a calming activity into an exercise in frustration.

My introduction to pipe smoking came via the same friend who introduced me to Scotch and cigars. He arrived at one of our Sunday coffee sessions with a gift, a briar pipe from the Italian maker Savinelli. It was in the classic "billiard" shape with a rounded bowl attached to a straight, tapered stem. The tight grains of the burl showed beautifully through the dark, polished finish on the wood, but to the trained eye there were a couple of pits in the briar that had been filled in with putty. Without those tiny mars, the pipe would likely retail for over a hundred dollars. Instead it was downgraded to a complimentary gift for tobacconists, which is how it made its way to being my starter pipe.

From my friend I learned the three-step method for packing a pipe that is passed down to many new pipe smokers. An initial pinch of tobacco is placed into the bowl and loosely tamped down. Then a larger pinch is added and tamped again, filling the chamber a bit higher. One last even larger pinch and one more tamp completes the process. Fill the pipe "first with the child's hand, then a woman's, and finally a man's," goes an old adage, denoting the increasing amount of tobacco added at each step. This deceptively simple procedure takes practice. Georges Herment's 1954 treatise on pipe smoking devotes six illustrated pages to the proper technique, cautioning that a smoker "who fills his pipe as he would the kitchen stove is treating it as no better than a cigarette and will certainly be paid back in his own coin."[2]

Then comes the lighting of the pipe, achieved by holding a match over the tobacco and lightly puffing. Time to smoke? No, not yet. First you let the tobacco burn itself out. Only then do you re-light and finally enjoy the pipe. If you have packed it properly, and if the tobacco is at the right degree of moisture, and if the pipe is clean, then it should continue burning with relatively little effort. But if these conditions are not met, you will have to constantly fiddle: re-lighting, re-packing, scraping away char or wiping away buildup with a pipe cleaner. That may all seem like more trouble than it's worth. On a good day, however, one is rewarded not only with the enjoyable aromas of fine tobacco but also with the satisfaction of having mastered an arcane art.

"The pipe is a unique invention of Man that has combined his creativity with the elements of nature: fire, earth, water and smoke, all of which co-mingle with the sky," writes tobacco enthusiast Richard Hacker in his typically extravagant style. "There is a certain mystique to it all, and, perhaps that is why, when you see someone smoking a pipe, you cannot help but think he knows something you do not."[3] From my own experience smoking a briar pipe in public, I can confirm that the practice tends to elicit curious conversation. The sight of someone doing so, especially a young person, has become rare. According to the *Wall Street Journal*, Americans smoked more than fifty million pounds of pipe tobacco in 1970. By 2009, that number had fallen to around just five million.[4] Though news articles occasionally note a resurgence of pipe smoking among young people, the trend never seems to stick.

Pipe smoking today is associated with older generations. In "Among the Pipemen," a lovely essay that appeared in the literary magazine *Granta,* writer Andrew Martin vividly captures this vision of the pipe smoker in fond recollections of his Uncle Sid:

> My Uncle Sid smoked a pipe. He maximized the soothing, ritualistic aspects of the process in that he not only wielded the pipe cleaners, the various prodding instruments of a pipe tool and the weathered, old-faithful tobacco pouch, but he also

rubbed his own tobacco, which came out of the tin solid, like a little piece of card. When these preliminaries were complete, and the flame was lowered on to the tobacco, there was what seemed like a crisis (not that Uncle Sid was remotely unsettled) as he discharged great clouds of smoke in the opening moments of combustion. This, to me, was as time-hallowed, as wholly masculine and right, as seeing a steam locomotive getting going. And in fact Uncle Sid was a train driver, and it was the contrast between his man of action persona – he was also a keen gardener – and the state he fell into with the pipe properly lit that I found particularly attractive. When Uncle Sid's pipe was up and running, so to speak, then the smoke streams issuing from him were almost invisible, and he seemed to exist in a different dimension. He might be referred to by those present (especially, and in rather aggrieved tones, by his own wife), but he hardly ever participated in the conversation himself. Well, he didn't need to: he had his pipe.

On those occasions when my father took me into pubs, I would focus on the Uncle Sid types, with their pipes in their mouths and their pipe paraphernalia on the table before them, forming a barricade between them and the outside world. The pipe was so obviously the priority with these men that I would wonder how those in their company could put up with being marginalized in that way. But I was on the side of the pipemen. Objectively, you might say they were under-weaned, but to me their pipes symbolized maturity and achievement. Pipes were not dashing or rakish, as cigars were in the nineteenth century and cigarettes in the twentieth; they were for men who'd graduated beyond trying to be 'cool', and I admired that, perhaps because I stood on the foothills of trying to be cool myself, and I knew it was going to be a hard slog.[5]

Pipe smoking has not become cool, but it's easy to imagine that it might have. After all, so many other goods emerged from their twentieth century commodification to be embraced as craft, artisanal, authentic, small batch, etc. The marketing invites parody, but one doesn't need a long memory to know that things have indeed gotten better. Coffee, beer, wine, cocktails, chocolate, fruits, vegetables, meat, you name it: Practically everything we eat and drink has improved in the past few decades, with consumers rewarding quality and not just convenience. Yet despite the predilection of chefs, cooks, servers, and bartenders to smoke, tobacco has been excluded from this gastronomic revival. Why is that?

It's not just the health risks. "If the danger of tobacco is undeniable, so is its exceptional flavor," noted journalist Wil Hylton in a wonderful piece he wrote for *The New York Times Magazine*.[6] Hylton had ventured to the Ardennes region of Belgium in search of an intensely flavorful variety of pipe tobacco called Semois. Enjoying a lunch of endive-wrapped ham smothered in bechamel alongside glasses of Westvleteren Trappist ale with one of the last remaining Semois producers, Hylton imagined a parallel world in which today's foodies acknowledge the pleasures of quality tobacco:

> I was struck by how unfamiliar the scene would have been to my American friends who have, in a fashion typical of our generation, embraced the current culinary boom with maniacal fervor, boiling obscure reductions to drip onto bits of fruit exploded by bicycle pumps in homage to Ferran Adrià, and yet, despite this globe-trotting gustatory zeal, haven't the slightest comprehension of the exquisite flavor that haunts tobacco. If the modern mythos of the kitchen had arrived a

decade earlier, before the vilification of tobacco was complete, the pipe might occupy a place on the palate alongside argan oil and hijiki and yuzu. Somewhere in the multiverse, there is an alternate New York City where the Union Square farmers' market brims not just with heirloom melons and leeks and squash but also with local tobaccos as vibrant as the Cherokee purple tomato.

There is much more to tobacco than mass-produced cigarettes; the leaf offers unique flavors that many creative chefs, bartenders, and baristas find enticing.[7] At the French Laundry, Thomas Keller experimented with desserts like coffee custard infused with tobacco.[8] In Tampa, Florida, Cigar City Brewing crafts beers inspired by cigars. Tobacco bitters appear on fancy cocktail menus (although this is unwise and illegal, given the potential for infusions to extract dangerous levels of nicotine). In France, distiller Ted Breaux crafts a liqueur called Perique that captures the essence of Louisiana pipe tobacco; it's a remarkable elixir with a light, tea-like quality, and alas, not imported to the United States.

It's not outlandish to envision briar pipes taking a spot alongside flannel, beards, and fixie bicycles as markers of hipster style, yet this outcome seems unlikely. Tobacco was one of many products to undergo the industrialization, commodification, and national branding that revolutionized the food and drink industries. But unlike many of those products, it has barely managed to recover its history from those processes.

Reading through various essays on pipe smoking, a sense emerges that something good and valuable is being lost to the forward march of time. Andrew Martin's *Granta* musings appeared, aptly, in an issue devoted to the theme "Lost and

Found." Wil Hylton's article recorded the vanishing heritage of the Manil family who continues to grow Semois tobacco for the ever-shrinking number of aficionados who appreciate it. A century ago, millions of tobacco plants were grown in the Ardennes region. Today the Manils are one of only three producers remaining. "This is our tradition," Vincent Manil says proudly. "Even if no one remembers, we remember." The Slow Food movement eagerly protects heirloom varietals of plants that people eat, but there is no Slow Tobacco movement to do the same for plants that people smoke. If a style of tobacco vanishes, it may be gone forever.

The Semois tradition lives on for now, but how long will it last, and what has caused it to become so endangered? Gazing at posters for long-lost brands such as Royal Semois, Vieux Semois, and Semois Selectionne, Hylton asked Vincent Manil the same question. His reply was simple and direct: the cigarette.

THE BIRTH OF BIG TOBACCO

I disagree vehemently with many of the aims and arguments of the contemporary anti-smoking movement. Here, however, is a point on which we thoroughly agree: The mass-produced cigarette is a terrible product that has taken millions of lives, and the world would be better off if it had never become popular. For many people alive today, the cigarette is the only form of tobacco they encounter with any frequency. But it wasn't always like this. The twentieth century — the "cigarette century," to borrow Harvard University historian Allan Brandt's dreadfully apt phrase[9] — was an anomaly both in the pervasiveness of smoking and its domination by Big Tobacco firms. The fierceness of today's anti-smoking movement is grounded in reaction to that era; no one wishes to see this history repeat itself. To contemplate potential futures in which the harms of tobacco are minimized and its pleasures are more fully appreciated, it's essential first to understand the factors that combined to allow cigarettes to become so deeply rooted in American society.

It would be unfair to lay blame for the rise of the cigarette on any one person, but if you wanted to single out a couple who were particularly instrumental, a good case could be made for James Albert Bonsack and James Buchanan Duke. Bonsack invented the first machine capable of mass-producing cigarettes, replacing costly human labor with highly efficient manufacturing. Duke possessed the vision to put those machines to use and the marketing savvy to popularize the cigarette, transforming it from a niche and ill-regarded product into a commodified, yet glamorous, part of daily life. Together they revolutionized the American market for tobacco.

Bonsack was only a teenager in the 1870s when he began working on his machine to automate the rolling of cigarettes. Most smokers at that time, if they smoked cigarettes at all, chose to roll their own. Purchasing wrapping papers and loose tobacco separately and doing the work yourself was more economical than paying a premium for someone else to do it for you. The then-leading manufacturer of cigarettes, Allen & Ginter in Richmond, Virginia, offered a $75,000 prize for anyone who could devise a machine to replace human laborers. This was no easy task. It was difficult to pack cigarettes consistently, the papers shredded easily, and loose bits of tobacco were prone to jamming up the works. Bonsack's tinkering eventually resulted in a machine that he believed was up to the challenge and he obtained a patent in 1880. When his machine worked flawlessly, it could produce more than 200 cigarettes per minute, matching the output of forty or more human rollers. [10]

Allen & Ginter installed the machine on a trial basis. For reasons that are unclear, they eventually decided against using it in production. Perhaps this was due to problems with keeping the machines running at full efficiency, but other factors may have included a conservative wariness of disrupting their established business model, concerns that consumers would react unfavorably to a machine-made cigarette, and of course the fact that adopting the machine would have required paying Bonsack his bounty. Whatever the reason, the firm rejected the machine, opening the door for an upstart rival in Durham, North Carolina, to lay claim to the future of smoking in America.[11]

James Buchanan "Buck" Duke entered the tobacco business in the shadow of Bull Durham, which had grown into the largest tobacco factory in the world by selling tobacco blends, rolling papers, and loose tobacco. Buck Duke initially pursued the same business, but he knew that in the long run he would need a different strategy to compete with the much bigger company. Aware of Allen & Ginter's success selling hand-rolled cigarettes, Duke introduced his own "Duke of Durham" line in 1881, packaging them in sturdy cardboard drawer-style boxes that protected the delicate sticks inside much better than the paper packs used by other brands. More importantly, however, Duke foresaw that the Bonsack machine held the potential to transform the industry by drastically lowering the cost of rolling cigarettes, which would give his firm the means to compete ruthlessly on price. Bonsack, for his part, was eager to find an American client. Duke acquired two of the machines to try out, and Bonsack supplied mechanics to keep them running smoothly. In 1884 they pulled off their first perfect day of operation, producing an output of around 120,000 cigarettes. The tobacco business would never be the same.[12]

Duke and Bonsack struck a deal: Duke agreed to take on as many machines as Bonsack could ship to Durham, massively increasing his firm's ability to produce low-cost cigarettes. In exchange, Bonsack agreed that Duke would pay royalties on the machines at least 25% lower than any competitor, providing Duke with a tremendous long-term advantage.[13] By 1889, Duke's firm had eliminated hand-rolling with the use of twenty-four Bonsacks, producing more than 800 million cigarettes and replacing skilled labor with simpler jobs such as loading and packing.[14]

Automation radically transformed the economics of tobacco. A skilled roller could produce a cigarette about every minute. By the turn of the century, the improved Bonsack and its various imitators could produce around 500 cigarettes per minute.[15] This enabled massive increases in annual output, from only 16 million manufactured cigarettes in 1870 to more than four billion by the late 1890s.[16] Economies of scale brought the costs of making cigarettes steadily downward, from a starting point of eighty cents per thousand to only eight cents by 1895.[17] The slashing of federal tobacco taxes in 1883 also helped lower prices. Duke of Durham, which had always been cheaper than imports, was able to drop its price by half and remain profitable.[18]

Other firms simply couldn't keep up with Duke's relentless increases in output, willingness to cut prices, and massive marketing expenditures. In April of 1889, Duke met with the owners of the four largest competing tobacco companies to convince them that it was folly to continue working against each other. They combined into the American Tobacco Company with Buck Duke at the helm.[19] Although the company would be broken up by anti-trust enforcers in 1911,[20] its basic strategy defined the tobacco business in the twentieth century: making cigarettes at low cost, successfully marketing them to new populations of potential smokers, and turning them into a ubiquitous consumer product that would gradually displace every other form of tobacco use.

BEYOND THE BONSACK

As important as Bonsack's machine was, it took more than just the ability to manufacture cigarettes cheaply and at a massive scale to enable the cigarette's market domination. Consumers also had to be persuaded to buy them. Although the Tobacco Trust looms large in history, most Americans were still taking tobacco in more traditional ways at the time of its dissolution. In 1912-13, the United States lagged behind the United Kingdom, Spain, Austria, Germany, Japan and Russia in per capita cigarette consumption; only about 5% of American manufactured tobacco sales were devoted to the product. Most Americans still chewed tobacco and those who smoked preferred cigars.[21] A decade later, however, it was observed that "the triumph of the cigarette over the cigar has been the triumph of machinery over handicraft."[22] It wasn't just machinery: Developments in agriculture, processing, and marketing, as well as war and the fight for women's equality, combined to bring about dramatic changes in the way smokers purchased and consumed tobacco.

One vital factor in shifting smokers' habits was a change in the tobacco itself. The tobacco leaf that helped popularize cigarette smoking differed qualitatively from the varieties used in pipes and cigars due to where the tobacco was grown and how it was processed after harvesting. The first and most important step after harvesting tobacco leaves is curing them to remove their moisture. Traditionally the leaves were dried in open air or suspended in barns and dried out with the intense heat of wood fires. In the 1800s, however, American growers began switching from smoky wood fires to cleaner burning charcoal. They also moved the fires to the outside of the barns, directing the heat inward using mechanical flues. This allowed for more precision, reduced over- or under-curing of the crop, and prevented fires from burning out of control and taking an entire harvest of tobacco with them. Aside from improving consistency, this development didn't much alter the coastal tobaccos grown in North Carolina and Virginia. These were dark, rich, and high in nicotine; they were similar to tobaccos grown in the Caribbean, with which they competed for use in pipes, cigars, and chew. Further inland, however, the less fertile soil produced a leaf that was lighter in flavor and color. These lighter leaves took on a golden hue when cured by the new charcoal-fired flues, leading them to be known as "Bright" leaf.[23]

Around the same time, another light-colored variety called Burley was found to grow well in Kentucky and Tennessee. Burley is particularly well-suited for absorbing flavors and sweeteners, which made it useful for producing chewing tobacco. Its destiny, however, was to join with Bright leaf to create the distinctive taste of the modern American cigarette.[24] This blend, pioneered by R. J. Reynolds during a shortage of Turkish tobacco, proved to be uniquely irresistible.[25]

The difference between leaf blends used in modern cigarettes and the darker varieties used in pipes and cigars wasn't merely cosmetic. At the molecular level, the smoke produced by cigarettes is more acidic than the alkaline smoke of cigar and pipe tobacco. Nicotine in the latter is readily absorbed by the membranes of the mouth, encouraging smokers to puff on pipes or cigars without inhaling. The lower pH of cigarette smoke doesn't offer as much of the drug to the body when puffed this way. The smoke is, however, much easier to inhale. Taking it deep into the lungs, where the tissues of the alveoli have a far larger surface area than the mouth, produces a strong, sudden hit of nicotine that is rapidly absorbed into the bloodstream.[26]

This inhalation encourages a different pattern of use. Smokers of cigars and pipes absorb nicotine more gradually. Cigarette smokers become accustomed instead to sharp peaks of stimulation, creating cravings that can only be satisfied by frequently re-upping with another smoke.[27] The unfamiliar potency of the cigarette brought on dependence in the smokers who took it up. Although this was not initially an intentional design feature of cigarettes, it was a boon to producers. Through accidents of agriculture and processing they created the most effective and addictive nicotine delivery vehicle ever devised. "The cigarette was to tobacco as the hypodermic syringe was to opiates," writes drug historian David Courtwright.[28] Contemporaries observed that cigarettes encouraged more compulsive use than older ways of smoking. "[Smoking cigarettes] is more like, in its effects and practice, the smoking of opium than of tobacco," contended W. A Penn in *The Soverane Herbe*, his 1901 history of tobacco. "[The] cigarette is a variety of the craving for absinthe and morphia."[29]

Yet marketing challenges still remained. Not everyone smoked and not every venue welcomed the activity. Popularizing cigarettes required shifting the boundaries of who could smoke and where they were permitted to do so. To this end, war was an indispensable ally to the cigarette companies. Going into the late nineteenth century, cigarettes were viewed as an inferior form of tobacco use, a habit of "dudes and college misfits."[30] That dismissive attitude was harder to maintain as cigarettes became the smoke of choice on the battlefront. The product's entry into the American mainstream began during the Civil War, when many potential smokers took to it for the first time.[31] But it was the First World War that fully cemented its place in the market. As cigarettes became a source of rare comfort for men in the trenches, anti-smoking sentiments that had been rising up amid the Temperance movement became impossible to maintain. In response to a question about how Americans back home could best assist the troops in Europe, General John Pershing replied, "You ask me what we need to win this war. I answer tobacco, as much as bullets."[32]

As if flipping a switch, the government turned from a potential foe of Big Tobacco into one of its biggest customers. A federal program supplied the troops with cigarettes, purchasing from the tobacco companies in a ratio equal to their pre-war domestic market share.[33] In a period of two years, the government supplied the military with more than five billion manufactured cigarettes and sufficient loose tobacco for rolling eleven billion more; only about 200 million cigars were sent overseas.[34] At the same time, organizations like the YMCA that had previously opposed cigarettes switched to patriotically supplying them.[35] Soldiers fortunate enough to make it home returned with a newly acquired taste for smoking. Over the course of the war, Americans' per capita consumption of cigarettes nearly tripled.[36] By 1922, cigarettes finally eclipsed loose leaf and plug to become the nation's highest grossing category of tobacco sales.[37]

What war did to introduce young male smokers to the cigarette, suffrage and the fight for equality did for young women. Smoking had been viewed as unladylike, but as women entered the workplace and took on greater roles in public life, adoption of the cigarette served as a particularly visible way to signify their equality. As the *Atlantic Monthly* put it in 1916, cigarettes became for smoking women "the symbol of emancipation, the temporary substitute for the ballot."[38] At women's colleges, smoking pitted administrators cracking down on the practice against young women who saw it as an expression of liberation. Female students could be punished with loss of privileges, losing their freedom to leave the campus or to go on dates for weeks at a time. Further violations could lead to expulsion. Clashes continued throughout the 1920s, but eventually the students prevailed. Colleges acceded to smoke-friendly places on campus and gender-based prohibitions came to be seen as sexist and outdated.[39]

Cigarette companies were happy to abet this perception. Marlboro, associated today with rugged cowboy imagery, first made its mark as an elegant ladies' brand touting its "mild as May" flavor. The brand explicitly pushed back against the idea that smoking was unsuitable for women. "Has smoking any more to do with a woman's morals than the color of her hair?" inquired one Marlboro ad. George Hill of American Tobacco styled cigarettes as "torches of freedom" and allowed his publicists to organize a feminist march in New York City featuring prominent women smoking openly in the streets.[40] The upshot was another decade of exceptional growth for the cigarette. Per capita consumption doubled over the course of the 1920s, due in part to doubling the pool of potential smokers.[41] (Incidentally, the taboo against women smoking in public was one factor leading to greater smoking indoors. Had women been socially permitted to smoke outdoors like their male counterparts, they would have had less reason to light up in previously smoke-free spaces.)[42]

While developments in agriculture, war, and women's equality were to some degree exogenous to the cigarette industry, the growth in sales was also due to highly planned and intentional marketing. Tobacco companies spent unprecedentedly massive sums advertising their products. While such advertising is often demonized as a means of hooking new recruits, it's not always easy to disentangle ads aimed at soliciting new smokers from those aimed at winning existing smokers over from one brand to another. Competition after the breakup of the tobacco trust in 1911 was fierce. In the two years following its dissolution, expenditures on cigarette advertising approximately quadrupled.[43] Though there were minor differences between brands, the truth is that branding itself was often more important than any feature intrinsic to the product. A lot of this spending, accordingly, was aimed at shifting existing smokers' loyalties.

The launch of Camel was a paradigmatic example. R. J. Reynolds had long resented the tobacco trust, and when it broke apart he wanted a brand that would return his own company to glory. Camel was the answer. The blend featured a pinch of Turkish tobacco and the illustrated camel on the pack played up its exoticism. A mysterious newspaper ad campaign stoked anticipation for the brand's debut. "The Camels are coming," proclaimed the first ads in the series. "Tomorrow there'll be more [camels] in this town than all of Asia and Africa combined," said the second. Finally, the third ad fulfilled the promise of the previous two: "Camel Cigarettes are here!" The gambit worked and Camel soon became the number one national brand.[44]

Other brands followed suit with varying degrees of flimflammery. Lucky Strike was arguably the worst offender, with the brand's "It's toasted!" slogan implying to consumers that its tobacco was less harsh than that used in other cigarettes. In truth, there wasn't anything unique about Lucky Strike's process.[45] The brand also boasted that more than 20,000 physicians agreed that Lucky Strikes were less irritating; the free cartons of cigarettes doctors received for saying so presumably had no influence on their judgment.[46] Employing a similar tactic, R. J. Reynolds gave away cigarettes at medical conventions and polled the attendees to ask what brand of cigarettes they smoked. This was the basis for the claim that "More Doctors Smoke Camels" — it was true on the day of the survey.[47]

Other marketing initiatives were more clearly aimed at reaching new populations of smokers. "Reach for a Lucky instead of a sweet" associated cigarette smoking with physical fitness, pitching the habit to consumers, particularly women, seeking to lose weight.[48] The inclusion of collectible cards in cigarette packs featuring actresses and athletes, a practice dating back to the 1870s, created desire among the young, or at the very least influenced the choices of their parents. The cards helped launch the hobby of cartophily, necessitating repeat purchases to complete collections.[49] Candy cigarettes, which the tobacco companies initially confronted as trademark violations, were soon welcomed with a wink and a nod as a way of building brand awareness in children.[50]

One easily overlooked development worth mentioning is the availability of safe matches. For cigarette smoking to become a constant habit throughout the day, smokers required a convenient source of fire. The familiar cardboard matchbook was invented in 1892, in the same period that mass production of cigarettes was transforming the industry. The two products complemented each other perfectly, the former easing enjoyment of the latter.[51]

All of these factors combined to massively increase cigarette smoking in the United States. At the start of the twentieth century, annual per capita consumption stood at just 54 cigarettes. By its peak in the 1960s, this figure had risen to more than 4,000.[52] With the development of Bright and Burley tobaccos and the invention of the Bonsack machine in the late 1800s, it was perhaps inevitable that the cigarette would grow in popularity over the ensuing decades. Other events — war, women's equality, marketing, and safe matches — combined to make the market domination of the cigarette extremely thorough. But cigarettes also had one other attribute that made them particularly adept at hooking smokers: an extremely effective and versatile means of delivering nicotine that worked to Big Tobacco's obvious advantage.

THE TUG AT THE SLEEVE

That it is difficult to quit smoking has long been recognized; recall that Las Casas noted in 1527 that the Spanish colonials who had taken up tobacco in Hispaniola found it "beyond their power" to give it up. Surgeon General C. Everett Koop released a six-hundred-page report on cigarette addiction in 1988, controversially grouping cigarettes with illicit drugs.[53] Koop wanted to require a label on cigarette packages warning that cigarettes are "just as addictive as heroin and cocaine." A representative of the industry-funded Tobacco Institute responded that "claims that cigarettes are addictive contradicts [sic] common sense" and that smoking "is truly a personal choice that can be stopped if and when a person decides to do so."[54]

There was still a pretense of debate as to whether cigarettes are addictive as late as the 1990s, although by that time the industry's representatives could hardly be said to be arguing in good faith. Tobacco executives' rejection of the plainly obvious truth was ridiculous, self-interested theater.[55] Yet placing cigarettes and opiates on equal footing struck many as equally absurd. Heroin is the classic example of the drug-centered folk theory of addiction. In this view, a drug takes hold of a user until they become utterly enthralled to its use, focused single-mindedly on scoring their next fix and willing to sacrifice anything or anyone to get it. One dose leads inexorably to another, until the addict is forced to remain continually under the drug's influence or face unbearable withdrawal symptoms.[56]

But this folk theory is naïve; the kernel of truth in the tobacco industry's denials is that our understanding of addiction does need to be embedded in personal choice. Millions of people do simply choose to give up smoking and there are presently more former smokers in the United States than there are current smokers.[57] The chemical characteristics of nicotine are an important part of what makes cigarettes addictive, but focusing exclusively on the drug's interaction with the body is overly reductive. The difficulty of quitting cigarettes is tied to their incredible versatility.

Gene Heyman, a research psychologist studying addiction at Harvard University, identifies four characteristics shared by most addictive substances:[58]

Temporal and probabilistic disparities in costs and benefits — Addictive substances offer immediate and certain pleasures, while their costs are uncertain and may not appear for many years. Binge drinking, for example, feels good in the moment, while the cirrhosis of the liver it causes may not appear until decades later, if at all. The alcoholic discounts uncertain future costs in favor of short-term pleasure.

Lack of self-inhibiting feedback loops — Ordinary goods are self-limiting: exercise leads to fatigue, food to satiation. Addictive drugs increase tolerance in a user, but they do not satiate; users are always left with unfulfilled craving. Furthermore, avoidance of withdrawal symptoms can exacerbate the need to continue consuming the drugs.

Intoxication — Resisting the lure of addictive drugs requires one to take a long-term view (a "perspective of global choice" in Heyman's terminology). Intoxication undermines a user's ability to consider long-term costs, increasing the appeal of immediate enjoyment.

Behavioral toxicity — Addictive drugs tend to undercut the value of competing activities. Being strung out on heroin or drunk on alcohol, for example, undermines one's ability to pursue professional or familial rewards. These drugs "poison the field." When professional or familial goals are perceived as unattainable, the relative value of using a drug increases.

Stimulants, opiates, and alcohol all fit neatly into Heyman's framework. Cigarettes, he notes, are a special case. The first two conditions clearly apply: The pleasures of cigarettes are immediate, the most deleterious health effects are distant and uncertain, and a smoker will continue lighting up to maintain a level of nicotine and avoid withdrawal. But the latter two conditions do not: Cigarettes as normally used are not intoxicating and their use does not significantly undermine one's ability to pursue ordinary activities related to work, family, and leisure, at least in the short-term. (The stigmatization of cigarettes and the spread of smoking bans does impose some social cost for smoking, but this cost doesn't yet compare to that of self-destructive drunkenness or opiate use.)

Does this mean that cigarettes are not addictive, as tobacco industry shills once insisted? Of course not. Instead, the compatibility of smoking with ordinary activities illuminates how cigarettes maintain their firm grip. Whereas drugs like alcohol and heroin undermine an abuser's ability to pursue other valuable aims, cigarettes insinuate themselves right alongside them. "Smoking filled a niche that was home to few if any other activities," writes Heyman. "[Prior] to smoking, there was no activity that accompanied horseback riding, driving, working at the office, and socializing. Thus, smoking occupied a niche which it had all to itself. This meant that even if smoking was not particularly rewarding, it would nevertheless remain the first choice from a local perspective."[59] In other words, smoking is so difficult to quit not because it offers the intense highs or lows of other drugs, but rather because its mild effects make it a gentle companion to so many other activities. An experienced smoker can integrate cigarettes into all kinds of daily routines: waking up in the morning, staying focused at work, calming down on the commute home, settling after dinner, relaxing after sex. As the motto for one brand of ciga-rettes expressed it, "Whatever the pleasure, Player's completes it."[60]

This idea is echoed in *Smoking: The Artificial Passion*, David Krogh's 1991 treatise on why people smoke. "People may want to go out and get *high* on amphetamines, they may want to get *low* on Quaaludes, but they seem to want to get *medium* on nicotine," writes Krogh.[61] The seemingly contradictory effects of nicotine have been noted since King James's *Counterblaste* in 1604. James mocked smokers for lighting up before bed to sleep soundly then smoking again in the morning to wake themselves up. We see similar uses today. Nicotine is a stimulant, yet smokers light cigarettes to relax. A light dose of nicotine is enervating; a heavy one can tranquilize an elephant.[62]

Despite James's skepticism, the versatility of nicotine is no illusion. The drug's interaction with the body is complex and scientists are still teasing out the precise details of its effects. It's well-established that the nicotine molecule activates some of the same nerve receptors that respond to the neurotransmitter acetylcholine (ACH), which helps regulate the autonomic nervous system that controls involuntary functions such as breathing and circulation. Smoking sets off cascade of events in the body that includes increased heart rate, increased blood pressure, and the release of adrenaline. When these responses kick in, nicotine acts as a straightforward stimulant.[63] Nicotine also triggers the release of dopamine, a neurotransmitter that can signal pleasure and reinforce rewarding behaviors.[64]

How, then, can nicotine be relaxing? Unlike ACH, which clears from nerve receptors to allow new signals to come through, nicotine forms a longer lasting bond that blocks receptors from receiving new transmissions. With enough nicotine to saturate the nervous system, responses to both nicotine and ACH will be impeded. Rather than stimulate, the drug begins to depress autonomic functions. Too much of it can put an animal to sleep or even kill it, inhibiting the body's ability to regulate its own breathing. Fortunately, inhaling cigarette smoke directly into the lungs is a relatively inefficient way of getting nicotine from the plant into the body, so smokers are able to control their intake to remain well below those levels.[65] By smoking repeatedly throughout the day, they maintain saturation of these receptors and ward off the stressful symptoms of withdrawal.[66] There are differences of opinion about exactly how well smokers can regulate their moods through nicotine, but it's clear that they are able to do so to some degree. In studies that put smokers in distressing situations —subjecting them to blasts of white noise, for example — they take deeper drags, presumably to help them relax. In contrast, when smokers are directed to carry out extremely boring tasks, they are able to mildly stimulate themselves to increase their concentration.[67]

That's how nicotine works in a lab, anyway. In the real world, set and setting complicate the picture. A report by the Royal College of Physicians notes that the reinforcing qualities of nicotine are relatively weak in animal studies when compared to other addictive drugs: "Thus, it may be that nicotine alone does not have the powerful addictive properties necessary to account for the highly addictive nature of tobacco smoking, and that addiction to tobacco reflects complex interactions between nicotine, other stimuli associated with the inhalation of tobacco smoke, and possibly other environmental, social or behavioural stimuli associated with smoking."[68]

As one example of how social conditioning affects the desire to smoke, researchers have noted that orthodox Jewish smokers experience weaker cravings when abstaining on the Sabbath than when forced to abstain on an ordinary workday.[69] The role of habits, expectations, and social cues in smoking behavior should not be overlooked. If addiction to cigarettes consisted solely of maintaining a constant level of nicotine, patches and gums that deliver the chemical would be far better substitutes than they've worked out to be in practice. Smokers could gradually wean themselves with decreasing dosages or just carry on using them forever. Yet quit rates using gums and patches are low.

The difficulty in quitting smoking is not simply a matter of enduring physical withdrawal, which lasts a short time. Long after the physical effects of dependence have dissipated, ex-smokers may find themselves longing to re-incorporate cigarettes into activities that now seem incomplete without them. These activities are legion, and almost anything could trigger the desire to light up.[70] "What made you take up smoking again?" I asked a friend who was back at it after four months without nicotine. "It was the night Prince died," he said. That was as good an answer as any.

"Smoking is the familiar tug on the sleeve," writes Krogh.[71] "People are tied to smoking as Gulliver was tied to the ground by the Lilliputians: through hundreds of individual threads."[72]

SLOW TOBACCO

Nearly a decade after I first read about the Belgian Semois tobacco mentioned at the beginning of this chapter, I set out to finally try some. I found a store selling it online and a few days later a gold foil-wrapped brick of densely packed tobacco leaves arrived in my mailbox like an artifact from the past. On a chilly fall afternoon, a friend and I met on the heated patio of a cocktail bar to sample it in our pipes.

Crumbling the brick into pinches of tobacco, we noticed that it was surprisingly dry. Compared to some blends, which can feel stickily sweet with flavorings, this was pure leaf and intensely strong. The aroma was more reminiscent of a cigar than typical pipe tobacco. Its lack of moisture made it easier to light, too. We packed our bowls and they ignited with barely any effort, air coursing through the leaves to fuel a cherry of burning tobacco, then onward through the stem to carry the subtly flavored smoke to our mouths, and finally exhaled into our surroundings. Paired with the crisp air and potent cocktails made with dark rum and Scotch, all the elements came together for a perfect autumn afternoon. We had the space mostly to ourselves, but our pipes were a conversation starter when people did join us outside. One patron thanked us for smoking. Though not a pipe smoker himself, he enjoyed being around the aroma. It's a remark I've heard many times while smoking a pipe or cigar, from smokers and abstainers alike.

Decades ago, two friends enjoying each other's company over drinks and pipes would have been an ordinary sight. In the present, we were aware of how anachronistic we appeared. Pipe smoking has plummeted. Most smokers in the twentieth century turned to cigarettes, and no one stops to thank them for filling the air with the scent of Marlboro or Camel. By the ordinary workings of the market and by coercive legislation, the places available for us to get together with a pipe have dwindled. A few years from now, who's to say whether the Manil family will continue to grow their Semois, whether the American government will allow it to be sold in the United States, or whether health officials will deign to let us have even this small outdoor patio on which to savor it?

It's easy to romanticize the past, focusing on the downsides of industrialization while ignoring the tremendous improvements in living standards and reductions in domestic labor that it enabled. Nonetheless, most of us would agree that when it comes to food, our lives have been enriched by the influence of "countercuisines," historian Rachel Laudan's term for culinary approaches that arise as a reaction against industrial production. Most notable of these is the Slow Food movement that sprung forth from Italy, emphasizing the preservation of traditional foodways and celebrating regional specialties.[73] Regardless of whether consumers buy completely into the ideals of Slow Food or other countercuisines, many have come around to demanding and appreciating higher levels of quality in their food and drink. They also take a keen interest in how the things they consume affect their health. Faced with endlessly conflicting and confusing reports of what is and isn't healthy, many have adopted the refreshingly simple advice of journalist and food preacher Michael Pollan: "Eat food. Not too much. Mostly plants."[74]

We do not yet have a Slow Tobacco movement. Even so, those who choose to smoke might take some cues from Slow Food. If cigarettes are the fast food hamburgers of the tobacco world, pipes and cigars are the slow-cured handmade sausages. Premium cigars are often literally rolled by hand and may spend years aging before reaching tobacco shops. The origin of the leaves that go into them affects their flavor. Even the time it takes to enjoy them stands in stark contrast to that of the cigarette. The latter is made for the five-minute work break, disposable, stubbed out halfway-finished if the need arises. A pipe or cigar, in contrast, requires a commitment of time. The pipe takes to time to pack, light, smoke, and clean. A large cigar could easily take an hour or more to smoke. When one lights one of these, one is affirmatively deciding not to be rushed. The need to slow down and savor the tobacco, appreciating its subtle nuances, is part of the appeal. For people who decide to experiment with Slow Tobacco, we might go so far as to offer advice mirroring Michael Pollan's for eating, urging most importantly to avoid the deadly and addictive trap of cigarettes: "Smoke tobacco, if you choose. Not too often. Mostly cigars and pipes."

This is not to say that any form of tobacco use is risk-free. But cigarettes differ from the cigars, pipes, and chewing tobaccos that they displaced from the market by more than just the characteristics of the tobacco used to make them. They are also worse for us. Cigarettes possessed the competitive advantages of being highly addictive, compatible with modern urban lifestyles, and cheap to produce. Social life adapted by allowing smoking to colonize previously smoke-free spaces and erasing taboos about who is permitted to smoke. The rising popularity of cigarettes soon revealed that this form of tobacco was not only exceptionally easy to inhale, but also exceptionally lethal. As the people who smoked them began dying in record numbers, it became clear that the cigarette was a modern, mass-produced, smartly-engineered package of addiction and death.

SMOKING GUN

One of the most common errors of the defenders of the cigarette is the confounding of cigarette smoking with tobacco smoking in general. While I am no friend of the cigar or the pipe, and believe the use of tobacco in other forms is but a lesser evil, I hold that the cigarette is in a class by itself and its evil effects are not those common to the use of tobacco in other forms.

— Hudson Maxim, *The Christian Advocate*[1]

SOON AFTER THE cigarette began its rise to conquer the American tobacco market, temperance advocates set out on a crusade to eradicate its use. Though their efforts are less remembered than the campaign for the Prohibition of alcohol, they attacked cigarettes with nearly the same vigor. They were surprisingly successful, too: From 1890 to 1930, bans on cigarettes were enacted in fifteen different states. Yet this period of anti-cigarette activism has been largely forgotten. "Previous writers, when they have taken any notice of this campaign at all, dismissed it as the work of a few crackpots firing from the lunatic fringe," notes historian Cassandra Tate in *Cigarette Wars*, her book relating the story of this movement. "The legislative record alone shows that it was more important politically than has been recognized."[2]

As cigarettes grew in popularity, they faced social opprobrium that other forms of tobacco use were spared. Employers expressed the anxieties of the era with bans on cigarette smoking among their workers. Thomas Edison was one vocal supporter of these policies. Though he contended that tobacco "aside from cigarettes does no harm to society,"[3] Edison believed that cigarette use was both a sign of bad character and an especially harmful means of smoking. He attributed the health dangers of cigarettes to the paper used to wrap them, an explanation that conveniently absolved his beloved cigars from posing any risk.[4]

Edison was far from alone in putting his opposition to cigarettes on a less than scientific footing. Allegations that smoking is detrimental to health date as far back as Europeans' first encounters with the habit, but the dangers of cigarettes would not be fully established in medical journals until the mid-twentieth century. Leaders of the first American crusade against cigarettes focused more on the moral dimensions of smoking than on its health risks. Henry Ford warned in a popular tract entitled *The Case Against the Little White Slaver* that "[if] you will study the history of almost any criminal you will find that he is an inveterate cigarette smoker."[5] Lucy Page Gaston, the anti-cigarette campaign's answer to the temperance movement's Carrie Nation, argued that lighting a cigarette was the first step on a path to moral degeneracy. She contended that cigarettes exposed smokers to a substance called furfural that allegedly triggered a thirst for alcohol; smoking led to drinking led to immorality, imbecility, and criminality.[6] (Gaston also believed that cigarette smokers were marked by "cigarette face," a malady whose precise symptoms are unclear but whose alleged sufferers included President William Harding.)[7]

The campaign against cigarettes mirrored the motivations of the broader progressive eugenics movement, grounding opposition in racist and sexist demands to preserve the Anglo-Saxon character of the United States. Early consumers of cigarettes were often urban immigrants from southern and eastern Europe or women working jobs of dubious moral repute. Cigarettes were deemed guilty by association. Progressive campaigners argued that women's weaker nerves made them particularly vulnerable to cigarette smoke and that the habit threatened their reproductive abilities. Keeping cigarettes away from the lips of Anglo-Saxon women was considered imperative not just for their individual health, but also as a means of guarding against racial degeneracy.[8]

The moral, racial, and anti-feminist elements of the first American anti-cigarette crusade set it apart from the mid-century campaign that was better informed by medical science. The medical establishment was largely unwilling to join the fight in this early period, withholding professional approval for anti-smoking legislation. Moral reformers like Lucy Page Gaston had the fervor but they didn't yet have the science. The popularity of cigarettes after the first World War, the identification of smoking with women's equality, and the backlash to alcohol Prohibition made potential allies wary of pushing too hard for the cause of banning them.[9] As a result, the anti-cigarette movement foundered and withered until the 1950s and 1960s, when it rose anew with backing from the medical community. This marked a new era in anti-smoking advocacy, one that was grounded in the science of epidemiology rather than anti-smoker moralizing. This scientific turn did, however, vindicate the Progressive Era anti-cigarette activists in one respect: When it comes to the dangers of tobacco, they had correctly discerned that cigarettes truly are in a class all their own.

AN UNPRECEDENTED KILLER

Even before the health dangers of cigarettes were subjected to rigorous scientific analysis, there was enough public perception of their risks that cigarette companies felt the need to market their own brands as healthier than their competitors'. "Not a cough in a carload" advertised a campaign from Old Gold;[10] "More doctors smoke Camels than any other cigarette" stated another from R. J. Reynolds.[11] Though deceptive in their aims, these ads were tellingly defensive. Awareness was in the air that the nation's cigarette habit couldn't possibly be healthy.

It had long been known that smoking causes irritation of the throat and that tobacco users are prone to oral cancers, but the link to lung cancer and heart disease was obscured. Epidemiology was just beginning to expand its purview from infectious diseases to lifestyle diseases, and the field required new analytical methods to do. Moreover, despite widespread tobacco use, lung cancer was a truly uncommon disease prior to the rise of cigarettes. Lung cancer was such a rarity in the early twentieth century that when tobacco researcher Alton Ochsner witnessed his first autopsy of a lung cancer victim as a medical student in 1919, he was informed that he might never encounter the disease again.[12] Instead the number of lung cancer victims increased to a steady trickle, then to a flood. Only 400 cases were reported throughout the United States in 1914, the first year that it was listed as a cause of death; in 1940 there more than 8,000.[13] By the end of the 1940s, incidence of lung cancer had increased at five times the rate of other cancers.[14]

Cancer had long been viewed as a tragic consequence of aging, but the sudden increase in lung cancer specifically suggested that there must be some external cause. In hindsight the culprit seems obvious, but at the time the idea that cigarettes were to blame met with skepticism, and not just from the tobacco industry. People had been smoking in some form for centuries, which created a puzzle as to why lung cancer was increasing at that particular moment. This was also a period of rapid social and technological change; other explanations, such as migration to the cities and exposure to industrial air pollution, car exhaust, and road tar, seemed plausible, too.[15] Paradoxically, the very ubiquity of cigarette smoking made it harder to identify the cause: Since so many people had become smokers, their high proportion among lung cancer patients didn't leap out from the background.[16] There was also the fact that many doctors were cigarette smokers themselves, and they were reluctant to believe that their daily habit might be killing them.[17]

Proving the case was an uphill battle that significantly advanced the science of epidemiology. Establishing cigarette smoke as a cause of lung cancer required collecting massive data sets, applying rigorous statistical methods, and demonstrating that the chemicals in cigarette smoke are carcinogenic. By doing so, researchers conclusively proved that the most profitable product for Big Tobacco was the most lethal for consumers.

1950 was a watershed year for this research, with independent studies from the United States and England linking cigarettes to the alarming rise in lung cancer. (Researchers in Nazi Germany had actually published studies on the topic a decade earlier, but their results didn't make an impact elsewhere and remained obscure for a long time. The story of their work is recounted in Robert Proctor's *The Nazi War on Cancer*.)[18] On the American side, a medical school intern named Ernst Wynder noticed the omission of smoking status from a lung cancer victim's medical record. Following up with the deceased's widow revealed that the patient had habitually smoked two packs a day. His curiosity piqued, Wynder interviewed more lung cancer patients at a nearby hospital. The high prevalence of smoking among them convinced him to continue with further research. He traveled the country to interview lung cancer patients, eventually accumulating data on nearly 700 cases.[19] These formed the basis of a landmark paper in the *Journal of the American Medical Association*. Wynder reported that more than 96% of the patients were at least moderately heavy smokers, that almost all of them had smoked cigarettes for decades, and that they consciously inhaled the smoke. Most strikingly, carcinoma of the lung rarely appeared in nonsmokers or minimal smokers.[20]

Parallel work was underway in England by Richard Doll and A. Bradford Hill. Out of 649 men diagnosed with lung cancer in their study, only two were nonsmokers. They also observed a clear dose-response relationship: The more cigarettes people smoked, the more likely they were to develop lung cancer. A quarter of the male patients in their study smoked more than twenty-five cigarettes per day. This finding helped bolster the case that cigarette use wasn't merely correlated with cancer, but was playing a causal role.[21]

As strong as these studies were, they had one deficiency: They were retrospective, beginning with an existing pool of patients and asking them to recall their past habits. This type of research, called a case-control study, is subject to recall bias, the possibility that patients who have been stricken with an illness will unintentionally overstate their exposure to risk factors. Thus, the next step was to undertake prospective studies that tracked groups of smokers and nonsmokers over time and compared their health outcomes. This kind of research, known as a cohort study, can take years to complete and may require the cooperation of thousands of respondents. In England, Doll and Hill utilized a listing of 60,000 doctors working in Great Britain. The doctors were invited to answer questionnaires regarding their health and smoking status, with periodic follow-ups. In the United States, Cuyler Hammond and Daniel Horn of the American Cancer Society led a team of 22,000 volunteers, comprised mostly of housewives, who collected data from more than 180,000 white men over fifty. The ambitious efforts of these two teams broke new ground in the study of public health.[22]

Preliminary results from Doll and Hill pointed strongly again to a dose-response relationship between cigarette smoking and lung cancer, and all of the lung cancer fatalities they recorded were of smokers.[23] The American Cancer Society results were even more striking. Cigarette smokers in every age category suffered an overall mortality rate far above that of nonsmokers. The heaviest smokers died of lung cancer at a rate more than ten times that of nonsmokers, and the absence of a rural-urban divide eliminated city air pollution as a competing causal explanation. Most alarmingly, the ACS study revealed that heavy smokers were not only at greater risk of developing lung cancer, but that they were also succumbing to heart disease at twice the rate of nonsmokers, suggesting that smoking contributed to a much more common cause of death.[24]

Skeptics suggested that perhaps smoking was merely correlated with the development of tumors or that the habit was a necessary but insufficient factor in their growth. There was even speculation that a genetic factor might make people both more likely to smoke and more likely to develop cancer. (This possibility was suggested by the statistician Ronald Fisher, who ignominiously capped his career with a sustained assault on the cigarette-lung cancer hypothesis.)[25] Research led by Ernst Wynder indicted tobacco smoke as a carcinogen by painting concentrated cigarette smoke onto the shaved backs of laboratory mice. While mouse skin was an imperfect substitute for human lungs — a fact that tobacco companies used to argue against his findings — the exposed mice developed tumors at a much higher rate than identical mice in an unexposed control group, suggesting a direct causal relationship.[26]

To any disinterested observer, the pioneering research of the 1950s settled the major questions surrounding cigarettes and mortality, culminating in the release of the landmark report of the United States Surgeon General in 1964 that tied heavy smoking to a 70% increase in mortality risk and a twenty-fold increase in risk for lung cancer.[27] The report decisively shifted public perceptions of cigarettes and initiated a steady decline in American smoking rates that continued for decades.

Since then, cigarette smoking has become one of the most studied research areas in epidemiology. We now possess a much more detailed picture of how smoke exposure leads to cancer mutations in the lungs and an abundance of evidence that more smoking leads to greater risk. A pooled analysis published in 2011 found that even light cigarette smokers triple their risk of lung cancer and that the heaviest smokers (consuming more than thirty cigarettes per day) suffer a risk up to fifty times higher than nonsmokers.[28] Cardiovascular diseases caused by smoking are estimated to be responsible for a roughly equal number of premature deaths as lung cancer.[29]

Estimates of the total mortality caused by smoking vary considerably since unlike deaths caused by discrete events such as car crashes and gunshots, it's not possible to simply tally up the deaths attributable to tobacco. Instead, researchers compare the prevalence of causes of death that are associated with smoking to the rate of smoking among various populations, attempt to account for other confounding factors, and give their best shot at an estimate of how many premature deaths would not have occurred in the absence of smoking. Despite this inherent uncertainty, there is no question that the rise of cigarettes has taken a tremendous toll in human lives. For the United States, current mortality estimates range from around 380,000 deaths per year at the low end[30] and up to a more speculative 500,000 at the high end.[31] Researchers disagree about specific figures, but there is no disagreement that cigarettes remain one of the leading causes of preventable death in the United States.

The global impact of tobacco use is even greater, especially in countries where rates of cigarette smoking are significantly higher. Though there are notable exceptions, such as Japan, a wealthy nation in which cigarette smoking is still culturally ingrained, smoking prevalence is gradually shifting away from countries with a very high development index to those with lower per capita incomes. Smoking rates approach or exceed 50% of the adult male population in parts of Asia, Indonesia, Eastern Europe, and Africa.[32] As a tragic result, the World Health Organization estimates that more than seven million deaths each year can be attributed directly to tobacco use.[33]

As is hopefully clear by now, although this book defends some forms of tobacco, it is by no means a defense of cigarettes.

Reducing cigarette use in the United States over the past sixty years has been a triumph of public health. Reducing it even further remains a noble goal, even if the means by which anti-smoking activists seek to do so are often problematic. But what of other ways of smoking? Many policies aimed against cigarettes end up catching pipes and cigars in the crossfire. And while no use of tobacco is completely safe, it's worth questioning whether it's sensible to treat all forms of smoking as equally undesirable.

A (VERY) BRIEF INTRODUCTION TO EPIDEMIOLOGY

Before digging deeper into the epidemiology of tobacco, it will help to make explicit some concepts in epidemiology that I've referred to only descriptively up until now. The most important of these is relative risk (sometimes expressed as an odds ratio or hazard ratio, depending on the type of study). This figure represents the difference in risk between a control group (nonsmokers, for example) and a group that's been exposed to the variable being investigated (smokers). If a study finds that the risk in each group is the same, then the relative risk is given as 1. When the exposed group experiences higher risks than the control group, the relative risk is greater than 1. A relative risk of 2, for example, would indicate a doubling of risk. A relative risk of 4 would quadruple it. If it turns out that exposure has a protective effect, then the relative risk would be less than 1 — obviously an unlikely outcome in studies of smoking.[34]

Relative risk is often the most important result of a study and it's the one most likely to be reported in media coverage, but the figure can be misleading without additional context. Relative risk is typically given alongside a confidence interval.

Think of relative risk as the research team's best estimate and the confidence interval as the likely range of values. By convention, the interval is typically given at the 95% confidence level, meaning that if the same sampling method were repeated many times, the calculated intervals would contain the true value 95% of the time. A relative risk of 2, for example, might be reported alongside a confidence interval of 1.5-2.5. A narrow confidence interval indicates a high degree of precision with regard to the size of the observed effect, whereas a broad interval indicates uncertainty about its magnitude. When the range of values in the confidence interval falls entirely above or below a relative risk of 1, the result is said to be statistically significant. When the confidence interval includes or straddles the value of 1, statistical significance has not been achieved, suggesting that the result may be due to chance.[35]

Statistical significance is a vexing concept, and it's important to note that it's not the be-all and end-all of scientific research. Sometimes a significant result is revealed to actually be a chance observation when later studies try to replicate the finding. Other times, a study that fails to achieve statistical significance might be suggestive of an effect that more powerful follow-up studies establish more definitively. It's also worth clarifying that statistical significance does not mean that a measured effect is significant to everyday life. A study might, by virtue of having an extremely large sample size, be able to detect very small effects that are real and yet so minor as to be irrelevant to most people's lifestyle choices.

Related to this is the fact that the relevance of any given risk depends on the frequency of the outcome being studied. A small increase in relative risk for a very common event can be more worrisome than a large increase for a very rare one. An example: Doubling your risk of dying in a car accident would be of much greater concern than doubling your risk of being struck by lightning, since fatal crashes are tragically common and lightning strikes are thankfully rare. Knowing the baseline frequency of the outcome in question is vital for putting an increased risk in context.

To apply these concepts to the example of cigarettes and lung cancer, studies have established that frequent smokers face relative risks more than ten times greater than control groups of nonsmokers.[36] This is an incredibly compelling result, and virtually no other common behavior has such a strong association with a lethal disease. Given the rarity of lung cancer in nonsmokers and the dramatic increase in risk for smokers, the cause and effect are inextricably linked. The link between smoking and heart disease is less obvious but no less real. Relative risk for heart disease among long-term smokers is estimated to reach up to twice that of nonsmokers.[37] That sounds less frightening than the ten- to twenty-fold increased risks of lung cancer, but the frequency of heart disease entails that even a small increase in risk can have a large effect on mortality. Cardiac diseases and lung cancer are estimated to be responsible for roughly equal shares of deaths attributable to smoking in the United States, even though fears of the latter are more vivid.

Despite decades of denial and obfuscation by tobacco companies, groundbreaking studies in epidemiology prevailed to convict cigarettes of being truly unprecedented killers. We also know, however, that modern cigarettes differ from earlier forms of smoking in important respects. The pH and flavor of the smoke that they produce is different, and so is the typical pattern of use. Cigarette smoke is uniquely suited to being inhaled deeply into the lungs, habituating smokers to lighting up again and again throughout the day. By comparison, smoking behavior involving cigars and pipes varies considerably, and as we'll see below, that variation leads to a notably wide range of different health outcomes.

WHEN THE MOOD AND CIRCUMSTANCES ARE PROPITIOUS

"We have no sympathy with prejudices against wine or tobacco used under the proper restriction as to the time and amount of consumption. A mild and sound stimulant with meals, and a cigar when the mood and circumstances are propitious, are not only to be tolerated, but approved." So read a dispatch in an 1879 issue of *The Lancet*, one of the world's leading medical journals.[38] It would be shocking to find a similar sentiment expressed in such a forum today. I came across the quote in an article citing it as an illustration of nineteenth century ignorance about the dangers of tobacco.[39] It's certainly true that the science of epidemiology has revealed a lot since then, especially with regard to cigarettes. But in fairness to those old authors of *The Lancet*, cigarettes were of only minor significance in the 1870s. The authors were addressing not the pack-a-day chain smoker, but rather the person "fortifying himself against fog and damp with the cheerful glow of a cigar in front of his face and the fragrant incense beguiling his nostrils." Although they got some of the science wrong, they acknowledged that smoking offers real pleasures, too. In that respect their attitude toward tobacco use was more sensible than that of the abstinence-only, anti-smoking hardliners of today.

Cigars and pipes receive less attention than cigarettes from health researchers, which is understandable since they are less popular and kill far fewer people; just assembling a representative sample of frequent pipe smokers for a study today would likely be challenging. The existing literature is complicated further by the need to differentiate between heavy pipe and cigar smokers and more occasional users, a crucial distinction that researchers often fail to include in the summaries of their findings. Nonetheless, applying modern methods of epidemiology reveals that although pipes and cigars certainly do carry some risks, they really are generally less harmful than the cigarettes that displaced them from the market.

This difference was evident in Ernst Wynder's original landmark study from 1950, in which he noted that cigarette smokers contracted lung cancer at higher rates than pipe or cigar smokers. Furthermore, the pipe and cigar smokers diagnosed with the disease reported very high rates of consumption: more than fifteen pipes or nearly seven cigars per day, much more than the typical smoker would light up. The observation that the frequency of smoking is strongly correlated to the risk of disease has held up in repeated in studies ever since.[40]

One of the most important studies on the topic was also co-authored by Wynder. In a retrospective study appearing in *Preventive Medicine* in 1988, he and his co-authors examined incidence of lung cancer among smokers of various kinds of tobacco and a control group of nonsmokers. Cigarette smokers, unsurprisingly, were by far the most at risk, coming in at sixteen times more likely than never-smokers to develop lung cancer (relative risk = 16). Smokers of cigars only, pipes only, and cigars and pipes together all fared better. Cases of lung cancer among pipe and cigar smokers were again concentrated among the heaviest consumers. The study reported that "[among] pipe and/or cigar smokers only, patients with lung cancer were more likely than controls to have been long-time smokers of 5 or more cigars or 5 or more pipefuls per day and to have inhaled." These heavy smokers suffered about three times the lung cancer risk of nonsmokers (rr = 3.2). At ten or more cigars or pipes per day, their risk climbed to nearly seven times that of a nonsmoker (rr = 6.7). Heavy consumers who reported consciously inhaling the smoke of their pipes or cigars brought on risk approaching that of cigarette smokers (rr = 12.3). For men who smoked fewer than five cigars or pipefuls per day, no statistically significant effect was observed.[41]

To put that another way, the *Preventive Medicine* study revealed that the more a pipe or cigar smoker's habits resembled those of a cigarette smoker — by lighting up many times throughout the day and consciously inhaling the smoke — the more their risk of lung cancer resembled that of a cigarette smoker, too. The results showed a strikingly clear dose-response relationship, which is bad news for anyone inhaling the smoke from multiple cigars or pipes every day. But the reverse is also true: The relationship suggests a lower risk for infrequent pipe and cigar smokers who do not deeply inhale the smoke.

Those findings are consistent with more recent studies on the topic. One of the most rigorous examinations is a cohort study published in *The New England Journal of Medicine* that followed about 17,000 men enrolled in Kaiser Permanente health plans over the course of more than twenty years.[42] Most of the men were nonsmokers, and researchers compared them to a group of about 1,500 who smoked cigars. The study differentiated between heavy cigar smokers (consuming five or more cigars per day) and moderate cigar smokers (consuming fewer than five per day). The heavy cigar smokers suffered substantial increases in risk for cardiac diseases, a near doubling in risk for all smoking-related cancers, and a tripling of risk for lung cancer. In contrast, of all the diseases studied in the moderate smoker group, only coronary heart disease showed a statistically significant increase, with a risk 1.2 times greater than that of nonsmokers. Other diseases suggested small increases in risk, but not at statistically significant levels.

Although the cut-off of five cigars per day is arbitrary — one certainly shouldn't conclude from the study that smoking four cigars per day is safe — the Kaiser Permanente study reinforces that the level of exposure to tobacco smoke matters. It's also notable that 76% of the cigar smokers in the study fell into the moderate group, reflecting a typical pattern of use that is less habitual than that of cigarettes.

Pipe smoking appears to be riskier than cigar smoking, though less dangerous than smoking cigarettes. A 2004 study by the American Cancer Society reported results from a cohort of pipe smokers whose health was surveyed for eighteen years.[43] Pipe smokers showed elevated risks at all levels of consumption, but mortality from smoking-related diseases was once again concentrated among the heaviest consumers. Men who smoked one-to-three pipes per day suffered about twice the risk of lung cancer as nonsmokers, but that rose to a nearly eight-fold increase among men who smoked eleven or more pipes per day. Other significant risk factors were the number of years of pipe smoking and the degree of inhalation. Pipe smokers who consciously inhaled were four times more likely to die from lung cancer than those who didn't. Laryngeal cancer showed the highest elevated risk among pipe smokers, although the estimate is imprecise given the small number of cases. Pipe smokers' risk of heart disease was only slightly elevated.

Another way to approach the relative risks of pipe, cigar, and cigarette smoking is to examine what happens when cigarette smokers switch to one of these other means of smoking. A study in the *British Medical Journal* found that although they end up consuming about the same amount of tobacco by weight as pipe or cigar smokers who have never used cigarettes, former cigarette smokers inhale the smoke more deeply. As a result, they show a mortality risk about 50% above that of pipe and cigar smokers who never used cigarettes. Even so, the study found that switching to pipes or cigars resulted in a 46% reduction in mortality risk compared to continuing to smoke cigarettes.[44]

The biggest and most consistent takeaway from studies of pipe and cigar smoking is that the level of exposure matters. Studies that aggregate pipe and cigar smoking at all levels do indeed find substantial risks, though these are still lower than those for cigarette smoking. But in studies that analyze moderate and heavy users separately, the risks associated with most smoking-related diseases show a strong dose-response relationship.

This conclusion is not the result of cherry-picking favorable results. In 2015, researchers at the Food and Drug Administration independently published a systematic review of twenty-two studies investigating cigar smoking. As one would expect, smoking is associated with higher overall mortality and with a higher risk of death from smoking-related diseases. But it found that the magnitude of these risks depends on the frequency and intensity of the behavior: "Mortality risks from cigar smoking vary by level of exposure as measured by cigars per day and inhalation level." Heavy cigar smokers and cigar smokers who also smoke cigarettes suffer the highest risks. Of the studies that examined men smoking one-to-two cigars per day, none reported statistically significant increases in risk for all-cause mortality or heart disease, and only one reported a statistically significant increase for cancer. Although some of these risks are likely slightly elevated, they are too small to be reliably detected. [45]

The observation that cigar smoking is associated with lower mortality risks than cigarette smoking is uncontroversial, although health authorities are understandably wary of high-lighting this conclusion. A monograph from the National Cancer Institute, for example, warns in bold type that "the risks of tobacco smoke exposure are similar for all sources of tobacco smoke." It then immediately concedes, however, that differences in inhalation and frequency of use tend to reduce that exposure among cigar smokers: "Most cigarette smokers smoke every day. In contrast, as many as three-quarters of cigar smokers smoke only occasionally, and some only smoke a few cigars per year. This difference in frequency of exposure trans-lates into lower disease risks."[46]

This comparison to cigarettes should not be taken to mean that pipes and cigars are completely without risk, as some smokers may wish to believe. I've spoken with smokers who assure me that cigars are safe and non-addictive. If only that were true! There is a degree of self-deception among pipe and cigar smokers who convince themselves that because the tobacco they smoke is more "natural" than cigarettes and is not deeply inhaled, it is therefore safe. The smoke from combusted tobacco leaves is by nature carcinogenic. While cigars and pipes are generally not as dangerous as cigarettes, use of any combusted tobacco product carries risk. Smokers who believe otherwise are fooling themselves.

The healthiest option, of course, is to refrain from smoking altogether. I hope that my summary of the data will convince anyone who smokes tobacco daily in any form to quit or cut back. But what of moderate use? The very idea is derided by anti-smoking advocates, who note that the concept of moderate smoking can be so malleable as to justify any level of consumption, no matter how excessive.[47] But although the concept is slippery, it's not meaningless. Unlike cigarettes, it's not unusual for pipes and cigars to be enjoyed infrequently. Official data is limited, but one recent survey suggests that primary cigar smokers in the United States tend not to smoke every day and to smoke fewer than two cigars on the days that they do.[48] The pattern of use for pipe and cigar smokers tilts toward more occasional enjoyment — perhaps literally only on special occasions, as with a celebratory cigar to mark a birth, holiday, or other life event. A variety of factors, including the pH of the smoke, the higher cost of premium tobacco, the greater time commitment, the need to carry accoutrements, the banishment of smoking from the workplace and public spaces, the awareness of health risks, and the stigmatization of tobacco use, all mitigate against pipes or cigars becoming a steady habit.

The scientific literature offers very little information specifically for the truly occasional smoker. In studies that differentiate between heavy and moderate pipe and cigar smokers, the range of use in the so-called moderate group often includes people who smoke multiple times per day. It's impossible to extrapolate from that to those who may go weeks or months without lighting up. Reliable data for such low levels of exposure simply doesn't exist. For people who smoke infrequently and do not consciously inhale, the dose-response relationship for smoking-related cancers suggests that any elevation in risk must be quite low. Cardiac risks may be a more salient concern, but these would still be small effects on a scale that may not be detectable.

One might also take an actuarial approach to the question. In the United States, tobacco users are the only group whom the Affordable Care Act allows insurance companies to charge elevated premiums. That raised the legal question of who counts as a user of tobacco. After considering a variety of options, the Department of Health and Human Services settled on defining tobacco use as the use of tobacco products four or more times per week.[49] A person who lights up a cigar only now and then does not seem to be a significant concern for the health insurance market.

The risks of very low-level tobacco use, to the extent that they can be measured, are commensurable with other lifestyle choices that many people would consider reasonable. One meta-analysis of studies relating meat consumption to coronary heart disease, for example, found that frequent consumption of processed meat brought on a relative risk of 1.4.[50] A prospective study of 44,000 men found that a heavily "Western diet" high in meats, refined grains, and sweets brought the relative risk of coronary heart disease up to 1.6.[51] Another study of diets high in smoked meat found that they more than doubled the risk of breast cancer.[52] Drinking a few alcoholic beverages per day is reported to double the risk of cancers in the mouth and throat; heavier drinking brings on five times the risk of a teetotaler.[53] One might read these studies and decide to give up meat, sweets, and drink entirely; many of us would certainly be better off reducing our intake. But few of us forgo all of them all of the time, nor are we typically stigmatized for enjoying them.

Pipes and cigars, if enjoyed truly only on occasion, likely fall into a similar continuum of risk. Whether that's a risk worth taking is an individual decision; the choice should be informed by medical science, but science alone cannot determine the answer. The nineteenth century doctors who wrote in defense of cigars lacked today's empirical knowledge, but they had the wisdom to recognize that cigars offer genuine benefits to the people who enjoy them. In my own life, I've concluded that the certain pleasures of lighting a pipe or cigar "when the mood and circumstances are propitious" are worth the small and uncertain risks that attend them when enjoyed sparingly. Millions of other consenting adults have made the same calculation. This puts us in conflict with today's abstinence-only preachers of tobacco control, who exceed even the early twentieth century temperance advocates' demands for a smoke-free world. Dressed in the trappings of science and public health, they seek to impose their values and preferences onto everyone instead of recognizing a diversity of legitimate lifestyles.

While the decision of whether to smoke remains, for now, a personal one, the matter of where one may do so has become increasingly political. Laws severely restrict the places in which one is permitted to light up, no matter how propitious the mood. In the latter third of the twentieth century, the focus of the anti-smoking movement expanded to include the divisive topic of secondhand smoke. Its aims shifted from merely discouraging smoking to forcibly banishing smokers from the public sphere. Although the modern advocates of smoking bans echo the scientific language of the admirable researchers before them who proved the dangers of cigarettes, their ideological zeal is more akin to that of the moralizing reformers of the temperance era. This absolute devotion to the cause has come at the expense of quality science. As we'll see in the next chapter, activists and researchers have dramatically exaggerated the risks of secondhand smoke in service of their ambitions to encroach ever more intrusively on the rights of smokers to light up in peace.

SECONDHAND NEWS

Falsehood flies, and the truth comes limping after it; so that when
men come to be undeceiv'd, it is too late, the jest is over, and the tale
has had its effect...
— Jonathan Swift, *The Examiner.*[1]

HELENA, Montana, does not often make global headlines, but in
2003 the small capital city became known for briefly achieving
one of the most astounding public health triumphs ever
recorded.[2] In June of the previous year, Helena had implemented a comprehensive smoking ban in its workplaces, bars,
restaurants, and casinos. The rate of heart attacks reportedly
plummeted by nearly 60% during the first six months of the
ban. Just as remarkably, when a judge struck down the law in
November of that year, the rate of heart attacks shot right back
up to its previous level.

For three anti-smoking advocates — local physicians
Richard Sargent and Robert Shepard, and activist and

researcher Stanton Glantz from the University of California at San Francisco — this observation was proof that smoking bans usher in extraordinary benefits for public health. "This striking finding suggests that protecting people from the toxins in secondhand smoke not only makes life more pleasant; it immediately starts saving lives," Glantz said in a press release.[3]

Newspapers ran with the story, credulously reporting that the sudden drop in heart attacks had been caused by the smoking ban. "The bottom line of Helena's plummeting, then soaring, heart attack rate is painfully obvious," warned an op-ed in *The New York Times*. "Secondhand smoke kills."[4] In the BBC, a spokesperson for Action on Smoking and Health used the study to promote a similar ban in Britain, suggesting that the "implication would be massive — there would be a dramatic fall in the number of heart attacks."[5] Wire services carried the result around the globe, and even the conservative *Wall Street Journal* cited it as an important finding.[6]

In the early 2000s, as jurisdictions across the country fought over expanding smoking bans to bars and restaurants, anti-smoking advocates seized on the Helena study and similar research to promote fear of secondhand smoke. Anti-smoking organizations claimed that just half an hour or twenty minutes of exposure to secondhand smoke imposes cardiac risks equivalent to habitual smoking.[7] Not to be outdone, the Association for Nonsmokers in Minnesota alerted the press that just *thirty seconds* of exposure could "make coronary artery function of non-smokers indistinguishable from smokers."[8] The message to nonsmokers was clear: The briefest exposure to secondhand smoke can kill you.

In the time since then, comprehensive smoking bans have proliferated globally. And now that more evidence has had time to accumulate, it's also become clear that the extravagant promises made by anti-smoking groups never materialized. Newer, better studies of much larger populations have found much smaller or no correlation between smoking bans and short-term incidence of heart attacks, and certainly nothing remotely close to the 60% reduction that was claimed in Helena. The updated science debunks the alarmist fantasies that were used to sell smoking bans to the public, allowing for a more sober analysis suggesting that current restrictions are more extreme than can be reasonably justified. Unfortunately, those fantasies get far more attention in the press than the more moderate studies that come along later to refute them.

As we'll see in this chapter, the cost of smoking bans has not fallen solely on smokers and the owners of smoke-friendly businesses. An additional casualty of smoking ban advocacy has been the scientific integrity of the anti-smoking movement, which has promoted fears that transient exposure to second-hand smoke is a lethal danger, that secondhand smoke kills more Americans than guns or cars, and that smokers them-selves are toxic. In its zeal to banish smoking from public places, activist researchers have allowed political expediency and ideological fervor to trump the truth about secondhand smoke, which turns out to be less scary than the public has been led to believe.

HEART MIRACLES

When the Helena study was published in the *British Medical Journal*, Glantz and his co-authors lowered the observed reduc-tion in heart attacks from 60% to 40% — still an impressive figure but a substantial drop from the claim they had prematurely publicized to press worldwide.[9] Immediate responses to the paper from other scientists were harshly critical, noting the small number of cases and the medical implausibility of achieving such a massive effect in such a short period of time. With so little data, it was impossible to know whether this was a real effect triggered by the ban or simply a chance occurrence.[10]

Nonetheless, the Helena paper spawned a wave of research seeking to replicate the finding. Studies observing similar reductions followed in places such as Pueblo, Colorado;[11] Bowling Green, Ohio;[12] and Monroe County, Indiana.[13] A shared characteristic of these places was a small population and correspondingly small sample size. The Monroe County study was based on a sample of only twenty-two heart attacks among nonsmokers over the course of nearly four years. When studies sampling larger populations finally appeared, the reported declines in heart attacks began to shrink. A study of the Piedmont region of Italy found a much lower decline of 11%, though curiously only among residents under sixty years of age.[14] England presented the first opportunity to study the matter on a national scale. Researchers there credited the ban with reducing the rate of heart attacks by just over 2% nationwide.[15]

Critics noted that the rate of heart attacks in England had been falling at similar rates in the years prior to the ban and that the decline could be attributable to many factors.[16] Regardless, the results there made it obvious that the miraculous reductions claimed in previous studies were unrealistic. Even so, despite acknowledging the wide variation in findings and the admitted methodological limitations of the studies, a 2009 meta-analysis conducted by the Institute of Medicine concluded that the impact of smoking bans on short-term heart attack rates was real and substantial:[17] "Even a small amount of exposure to secondhand smoke... can cause a heart attack," one member of the IOM panel informed *The New York Times*, urging that "smoking bans need to be put in place as quickly as possible."[18]

The IOM report had, however, omitted one of the largest studies of secondhand smoke and heart attacks conducted to date. A 2008 study covering the entire country of New Zealand — a population smaller than England's, but bigger than the American towns previously studied — found no significant effects on heart attacks or unstable angina in the year following implementation of a smoking ban; hospitalizations for the former had actually increased.[19]

Contradictory research continued to emerge. A clever study led by researchers at RAND Corporation in 2010 tested the possibility that the stunning reductions observed in small communities were actually due to chance.[20] They assembled a massive data set that allowed them to simulate studies like those in Helena, Pueblo, and Bowling Green on an unprecedented scale. Whereas those studies had compared just one small community to another, the RAND paper compared all possible pairings of communities affected by smoking bans to all possible controls, creating more than 15,000 pairings. They stratified results by age in case there were differential effects on the young, working age adults, or the elderly. And in an improvement on most other studies, they also controlled for existing trends in the rate of heart attacks.

The RAND researchers found no statistically significant decrease in heart attacks among any age group. Their data also suggested that fluctuations in heart attack rates were common in small populations, indicating that comparisons of such communities would frequently turn up dramatic reductions due purely to chance; large *increases* in heart attacks happened about as often. This explained the headline-grabbing results in places like Helena that were impossible to replicate in more populous jurisdictions. The conclusion of the study was blunt: "We find no evidence that legislated U.S. smoking bans were associated with short-term reductions in hospital admissions for acute myocardial infarction or other diseases in the elderly, children or working age adults."

A 2012 study of six American states that passed smoking bans reached a similar conclusion.[21] So did a 2014 study, which is notable for being co-authored by researchers who had previously published studies reporting post-smoking ban declines in the Colorado towns of Pueblo and Greeley. When Colorado enacted a statewide ban, the authors used the opportunity to see if their earlier results could be duplicated across the larger population of nearly five million people. No effect appeared. As an additional test, they re-examined the data excluding eleven jurisdictions that had previously implemented comprehensive smoking bans. The statewide ban still showed no effect.[22]

In an admirably honest commentary, the authors reflected on the reasons that earlier studies, including their own, had overstated the impact of smoking bans. The first is that small sample sizes allowed random fluctuations in data to be mistaken for real effects. The second is that most previous studies failed to account for existing downward trends in the rate of heart attacks. The third is publication bias: Since no one believes that smoking bans increase heart attacks, few would have bothered submitting or publishing studies that showed a positive correlation or null effect. Thus, the published record is likely biased, intentionally or not, toward showing a larger effect than truly exists.

The medical explanation for how secondhand smoke could trigger heart attacks is that exposure reduces blood flow, increases platelet aggregation, and causes endothelial dysfunction — all of which plausibly could cause long-term damage with chronic exposure. But the most well-conducted research suggests that the impact in the short-term is not as significant as feared. And in the places where declines in heart attacks were observed, reductions in secondhand smoke exposure might not have been the primary cause. A thorough paper published in 2016 by lead author Vivian Ho, an economist at Rice University, considered other factors that may have been overlooked in previous studies. Drawing on data from twenty-eight states over seven years, Ho compared rates of hospitalization for heart attacks in areas with and without smoking bans. When replicating the methodology of previous studies, she and her coauthors observed a small but statistically significant reduction in hospitalizations for heart attacks and congestive heart failure following implementation of a smoking ban, though only among people older than 65. But when they went a step further by adjusting their analysis with county-by-county health data addressing variables such as access to hospitals and increases in cigarette taxes, the apparent effect of the smoking bans vanished. Ho suggests that modest improvements in cardiac health that were previously credited to smoking bans may actually reflect differences in access to medical care and the fact that people smoke less when taxes increase.[23]

In the recent literature, the most notable study finding a correlation between smoking bans and the rate of heart attacks is a 2012 paper in *Health Affairs*.[24] It is arguably the strongest of the studies documenting a reduction, though it applies only to senior populations and did not adjust for tobacco taxes. But even researchers sympathetic to the claim that smoking bans substantially reduce heart attacks now concede that the larger the population studied, the smaller the observed effect. A 2013 meta-analysis noted that "studies with smaller population in the United States usually reported larger reductions ... while larger studies reported relatively modest reductions."[25] Or, to restate this in light of the most recent research, the largest studies often report no reduction at all.

Glantz disputed Vivian Ho's conclusion, suggesting that use of a different statistical model would turn up an effect.[26] But the dramatic reductions that he and other smoking ban advocates promised were so unbelievably massive that they would have stood out using any plausible model. Instead, in the time since the alleged Helena Miracle, they have retreated from claiming a 60% reduction in heart attacks to debating whether effects are illusory or just too small to be reliably detected. That says a lot about how far expectations have been lowered. As they say in the old Virginia Slims ads, "You've come a long way, baby!"

The myth that banning smoking in bars and restaurants will bring about astounding reductions in the rate of heart attacks is now dead and buried in the scientific literature, but for years the false promise of heart miracles has influenced public debate. That's just one justification for the bans, however. What about the worry that secondhand smoke causes lung cancer? Here, too, the fears propagated by smoking ban advocates have proven to be more frightening than the reality.

NONSMOKING WIVES MARRIED TO SMOKING SPOUSES

When anti-tobacco advocates began seeking restrictions on

public smoking, it became politically useful to identify harms caused by secondhand smoke. No matter how harmful cigarettes are to the individual user, it's difficult to justify restrictions on where to smoke them if they are a purely private vice. But if smoking is a public vice — if secondhand smoke puts the health of innocent bystanders at risk — then there are reasons for restricting behavior. Surgeon General Jesse L. Steinfeld laid out the strategy explicitly in 1971, suggesting that the anti-smoking movement should focus on harms to nonsmokers and re-define the right to smoke as the "right to pollute."[27] This was echoed by Stanton Glantz, who advised mimicking the environmental movement. "Activists should state that they are not 'anti-smoker' but rather environmentalists concerned with clean indoor air for everyone," he wrote in a 1987 editorial. "The issue should be framed in the rhetoric of the environment, toxic chemicals, and public health rather than the rhetoric of saving smokers from themselves or the cigarette companies."[28]

In an era in which permitting smoking just about everywhere was the default, odor and annoyance were sufficient reasons for nonsmokers to desire cleaner air. Absent medical harms, however, proposals to ban smoking legislatively reeked of paternalism. Establishing environmental tobacco smoke [ETS] as actually dangerous offered a way of putting a fig leaf on these nakedly restrictive policies. Thus, beginning in the 1970s, researchers and activists began hunting for evidence that secondhand smoke posed a lethal threat to those who inhaled it.

British journalist Christopher Snowdon, who covers the ETS controversy at length in his 2009 book *Velvet Glove, Iron Fist*, notes that the motivations of secondhand smoke researchers differed from those of the pioneering doctors who established the link between lung cancer and smoking in the

1940s and 1950s. Those doctors were investigating a genuine epidemic of lung cancer; the bodies were piling up and their work established beyond a reasonable doubt that cigarettes were the cause. Research on secondhand smoke reversed that approach. Scientists started out with a hypothesis — that secondhand smoke was causing lung cancer in nonsmokers — and took on the task of finding the bodies.[29] But what if there weren't many bodies to be found? The effort to prove the case in spite of that led to some rather biased detective work.

The first quality epidemiological study linking secondhand smoke exposure to lung cancer came from Japan and examined nonsmoking women whose husbands were smokers. Smoking was extremely common among Japanese men in the 1960s and 1970s, but it was considered socially unacceptable among women. This made Japanese wives a promising research population for uncovering dangers posed by secondhand smoke. Dr. Takeshi Hirayama of Tokyo's National Cancer Center conducted a prospective study of more than 90,000 Japanese nonsmoking women, classifying their level of exposure by their husbands' smoking rates and tracking the onset of various cancers for more than a decade. In 1981 he published the results in the *British Medical Journal*, reporting moderately elevated risks of lung cancer for wives of smokers compared to women married to nonsmokers (relative risks of 1.61 for wives of ex-smokers or of men who smoked fewer than twenty cigarettes per day, and 2.08 for wives of heavy smokers).[30]

There were potential confounding factors that Hirayama's work could not account for, but the sample size was large, the research came from a well-conducted cohort study, and the association with lung cancer showed a dose-response relationship. Hirayama's results were corroborated by a Greek study, although it was smaller and used the less reliable case-control method.[31] While far from the last word on the subject, these studies were suggestive of risks attributable to ETS and demonstrated the need for further research. They also made clear that the risks associated with secondhand smoke were of a lower level of magnitude than those associated with actual smoking. That made these risks much harder to detect and, given the political stakes, battles over how to interpret results became exceedingly heated.

INSTRUMENTALIZING SCIENCE, ENFORCING ORTHODOXY

In contrast to the groundbreaking research of the 1950s that forcefully demonstrated the causal link between cigarette smoking and lung cancer, the indictment of secondhand smoke emerged from a fog of contradictory empirical results. As explained in the previous chapter, relative risks greater than 1 indicate an association with disease; relative risks for smoking and lung cancer are often in the range of 15 to 20 and are even higher in the heaviest smokers. The relative risks observed in studies of secondhand smoke are far lower. One of the strongest studies linking ETS to lung cancer found a relative risk of 1.29, climbing to 3.25 among women who were exposed to ETS for their entire lives.[32] The results of other research were less favorable to the hypothesis. A Chinese study published in 1990 found a statistically significant relative risk of 0.7 — that is, wives with smoking spouses were observed to have lower risk than controls.[33] Many studies managed to discern no statistically significant findings at all. Others observed larger effects, but they tended to be less reliable due to methodology, small sample size, or both.[34]

The evidence supporting the hypothesis that ETS is a substantial cause of lung cancer was rather mixed. Nonetheless, anti-tobacco forces were determined to act as though the link were proven. Surgeon General C. Everett Koop said as much in his 1986 report calling for smoke-free workplaces.[35] Even those sympathetic to the cause, including Pulitzer Prize-winning journalist Richard Kluger, acknowledged that Koop was getting ahead of the evidence. "[Without] a doubt Koop was on the side of the angels," Kluger reported in *Ashes to Ashes*, his monumental history of cigarettes, "but without much doubt, either, he was in this instance using dubious means — shaky science — to justify the worthy end of achieving a healthier society."[36]

The Environmental Protection Agency issued its own report on the risks of secondhand smoke in 1992, conducting a meta-analysis of the existing literature. The selection and weighting of studies in the meta-analysis was questionable, and the agency abandoned its usual practice of using a 95% confidence interval, opting for a less rigorous 90% interval. These decisions appeared to be motivated by a desire to reach a pre-determined conclusion. Indeed, the agency conceded that its use of an atypically forgiving statistical test was justified by "the *a priori* hypothesis... that a positive association exists between exposure to ETS and lung cancer." Even with these factors working to buttress the hypothesis, the EPA saddled second-hand smoke with a relative risk of only 1.19.[37] The tobacco industry responded by suing the EPA for violating its own standards of evidence. In 1998, a court ruled decisively against the agency, determining that the "EPA publicly committed to a conclusion before research had begun," "adjusted established procedure and scientific norms to validate the Agency's public conclusion," and "disregarded information and made findings on selective information."[38] (In 2002 the Fourth Circuit of Appeals dismissed the entire lawsuit on narrow legal grounds that did not address the issues of science raised in the earlier decision.)[39]

Within professional tobacco control, activists enforced orthodoxy by publicly attacking researchers who published results contrary to the aim of indicting ETS. The most notable example was a 2003 study by epidemiologists James Enstrom and Geoffrey Kabat. Their research drew on a long-running database maintained by the American Cancer Society that tracked a cohort of Americans from 1959 to 1998. Enstrom's previous research had been funded by the ACS and that relationship allowed him access to extend the data further than previous studies. Enstrom and Kabat obtained information from 3,100 never-smokers regarding their exposure to ETS at home, work, and in other settings, resulting in a uniquely long-lived data set spanning 39 years.[40]

To the distress of anti-smoking groups, Enstrom and Kabat's study failed to provide evidence that secondhand smoke exposure increased the risk of lung cancer or coronary heart disease.[41] They were viciously attacked as shills for Big Tobacco even before their paper was published in the *British Medical Journal*. It was true that funding for their final years of research came from tobacco companies via the Center for Indoor Air Research, but Enstrom and Kabat's initial data was provided by the American Cancer Society and Kabat supported indoor smoking bans. Their sample drew from a large population and their results were consistent with other research in the field. In a less ideologically charged atmosphere, their work would have been weighed more or less equally with other inquiries that found results more to the anti-smoking movement's liking.[42]

Instead, Enstrom and Kabat's paper elicited a barrage of angered reactions. An editor of the *BMJ* noted that more than

140 readers submitted written responses, but that only 3% of these referenced actual data in the study. "It got bitter, and at times personal," she concluded. "A great read for anyone who enjoys a scrap. Disappointing for readers looking for a dispassionate appraisal of Enstrom and Kabat's study and its implications."[43] The debate was so inflamed that it inspired a paper in the sociology journal *Public Understanding of Science*. Entitled "Silencing Science," it noted that Enstrom and Kabat's critics overwhelmingly responded with "sarcasm and moral indignation" rather than addressing the merits of their work. While taking no position on the secondhand smoke controversy themselves, the sociologists concluded that responses strayed far from the ideal of dispassionate science open to following wherever the evidence leads. "There are elements of an authoritarian cult involved here: uphold the truth that secondhand smoke kills — or else!"[44]

Among ideologically committed anti-smoking researchers, this truth was settled science. From outsiders' perspectives, it was obvious that this research agenda had a pre-determined outcome. Historian Virginia Berridge memorably described the danger of secondhand smoke as a "scientific fact waiting to emerge."[45] New methods in epidemiology made it possible to investigate the question, and the desire to banish smokers from public spaces made it politically useful to do so. Lawrence Gostin, professor of law at Georgetown University and an editor of the *Journal of the American Medical Association*, offered a similar assessment. Research into secondhand smoke was motivated not by a crisis in public health, but rather by "the increasingly intense secular value that smokers were becoming a public nuisance." Gostin continues: "The scientific investigations that ensued purported to be neutral assessments of the health consequences, but they had significant design defects, were based upon moral (as well as scientific) assumptions, and had squarely in mind a set of preconceived policies the investigators hoped the research would support."[46]

That body of research culminated in the 2006 Surgeon General's report, which concluded definitively that secondhand smoke causes lung cancer.[47] This report is arguably the most thorough summary of the evidence, yet the associations buried in the text are less compelling than what one might expect from the damning condemnations in the Surgeon General's public statements. The report's table of meta-analyses puts the relative risks of lung cancer for nonsmoking spouses or employees exposed to ETS in the range of 1.12 at the low end to 1.43 at the high end. These are low by epidemiological standards, especially for a disease that is so rare among nonsmokers. (One of the meta-analyses even suggests the implausible result that children who are exposed to tobacco smoke are less likely to develop lung cancer as adults, with a relative risk of 0.81.)[48]

Ultimately, one can fairly say that although a causal link between secondhand smoke and lung cancer likely does exist at high levels of exposure, the effect is too small to be reliably detected even in powerful studies. Despite decades of searching, the most thorough research finds only small effects, and many studies fail to find any statistically significant effect at all. This stands in stark contrast to the studies of the 1950s that proved beyond any reasonable doubt that cigarette smoking was causing the lung cancer epidemic. For all the certainty that the Surgeon General and anti-smoking activists have expressed in convicting secondhand smoke, they have been unable to turn up such an obvious smoking gun. They argue instead that one must rely on the totality of the evidence. That's sound advice, but it's also a judgment call that leaves room for one's personal biases to color the findings.

With that in mind, it's illuminating to look at how contemporary research on the question has been received now that the aim of legislating smoking bans has transitioned from a hotly contested political issue to a *fait accompli*. Researchers at Stanford University and other institutions tracked the health of more than 75,000 women for more than a decade on average, gathering data on the women's smoking status and exposure to secondhand smoke in childhood, at home, and in the workplace. They published the results in 2013.[49] As expected, women who smoked were thirteen times more likely to develop lung cancer than never-smokers. Former smokers were four times as likely. Exposure to secondhand smoke, however, showed no statistically significant effect on the incidence of lung cancer at any level of exposure. Only women who lived with smokers for thirty years or more came close to showing a statistically significant relationship. This research essentially replicated the controversial findings of Enstrom and Kabat from a decade earlier, so one might expect that it ignited a similar firestorm of criticism. Instead it was greeted with a shrug.

Discussing the findings in the *Journal of the National Cancer Institute* — decidedly not a pro-tobacco publication — other researchers were surprisingly frank about the weakness of the association. "Passive smoking has many downstream health effects," said Dr. Jyoti Patel of the Northwestern University School of Medicine, "but only borderline increased risk of lung cancer… The strongest reason to avoid passive cigarette smoke is to change societal behavior: to not live in a society where smoking is a norm." Dr. Gerard Silvestri of the Medical University of South Carolina noted that "with regard to passive smoke, it's only the heaviest exposure that produces the risk. We kind of knew that before, but it's a little stronger here… We've gotten smoking out of bars and restaurants on the basis of the fact that you and I and other nonsmokers don't want to die. The reality is, we probably won't."[50]

In previous decades, any researcher caught saying such a thing would have been hounded relentlessly by their peers and scrutinized for the most tenuous ties to Big Tobacco. What changed? Not the science, but the politics. Now that bans have spread far and wide with no sign of being repealed, health authorities are more willing to confess what the skeptics have been saying all along: That the research investigating the link between secondhand smoke and lung cancer is more mixed than people realize, that risks are detectable only at the highest levels of exposure, and that enthusiasm for smoking bans has more to do with controlling behavior than it does with protecting nonsmokers from harm.

Two misleading perspectives on secondhand smoke

The debates over secondhand smoke that spanned the 1980s to early 2000s divided sharply over the question of whether health effects existed at all. Anti-smoking activists, motivated by the desire to legislate smoking bans, were invested in the conclusion that secondhand smoke kills. Tobacco companies were equally motivated to profess that it didn't. By placing the debate in such an obviously instrumental framing, both sides obscured more relevant questions about the magnitude of the alleged effects. The hidden consensus is that most of the risks worth worrying about require years of sustained exposure and that the risks that do exist are far less substantial than those associated with active smoking.

In order to build support for smoking bans, however, advocates found ways to make these minor risks loom large in the public imagination. When Surgeon General Richard Carmona released his 2006 report on secondhand smoke, he delivered it with a quotable, alarming statement that continues to be dragged into service whenever smoking restrictions are debated: "There is no risk-free level of exposure to secondhand smoke."[51] It naturally follows that any policies falling short of completely banning smoking are inadequate for protecting public health. "Smoke-free environments are the only approach that protects nonsmokers from the dangers of secondhand smoke," Carmona told the press.[52]

It's a memorable line, but what does "no risk-free level" actually mean? Our lives are awash in risk and living sensibly is a matter of weighing trade-offs. Riding in a car is objectively one of the most dangerous things we do, with nearly 40,000 Americans perishing in automobile accidents every year.[53] Yet millions of us drive daily without a moment's hesitation, despite there being no risk-free level of car use. Many of the foods we eat and the beverages we drink make it incrementally more likely that we will die prematurely, but few us would be persuaded to give up an occasional indulgence by the argument that there is no risk-free level of hamburgers, cake, or beer. In any other context, such language would rightfully be perceived as absurd.

For most toxic substances, scientists adhere to the dictum that the dose makes the poison and acknowledge that the cost of achieving zero exposure often exceeds the benefit. And that's for things that no one desires for their own sake, such as lead or arsenic in water, both of which are permitted in trace amounts. Some people do want to smoke, so there's no getting to zero without imposing costs on them. But is zero exposure a necessary goal? Is the smoke from a burning tobacco leaf really so uniquely toxic that reasonable people ought to fear that any exposure at all might kill them?

In a word, no. The former Surgeon General's "no risk-free level" statement is an unscientific cop-out that avoids the hard work of doing measurement and contemplating trade-offs. It stigmatizes smokers and induces paranoia in nonsmokers while being devoid of all but the most trivial meaning. Knowing that there are some risks at some levels of exposure is not the same as knowing what those risks and levels are. It's an excuse to demonize even the most transient whiff of tobacco, equating a brief encounter with a smoker on a city street to decades of living beside a chain-smoking spouse. It tells us nothing about which exposures we should avoid and which we can sensibly tolerate as members of a diverse, liberal society.

In *The Cult of Statistical Significance*, economists Stephen Ziliak and Deirdre McCloskey memorably dub this way of thinking the "sizeless stare." By this they mean that it's a flawed approach to science that values statistical significance above all other considerations. Researchers run their regressions, or they review the published literature, and the only question they ask is *whether* an effect exists. "Yes or no, they say, and then they stop. They have ceased asking the scientific question 'How much is the effect?' And they have therefore ceased being interested in the pragmatic questions that follow: 'What Difference Does the Effect Make?' and 'Who Cares?' They have become, as we put it, 'sizeless.'"[54]

To the partisans of tobacco control, if any health effect caused by secondhand smoke can be measured, no matter how small, then any intervention is justified, no matter how extreme. But as Ziliak and McCloskey hammer home, statistical significance alone is incapable of settling such arguments:

[Every] inference drawn from a test of statistical significance is a "decision" involving substantive loss and, further, not merely one narrow sort of loss under conditions of random sampling. Every decision involves cost and benefit, needs and wants, choices and courses… Accepting or rejecting a test of significance without considering the potential losses from the available courses of action is buying a pig in a poke. It is not ethically or economically defensible.[55]

The logic of the sizeless stare was explicitly adopted by Stanton Glantz in response to my criticism of his miraculous findings in Helena. "While we found a 40% drop in the 6 months we studied, the true drop could have been anywhere between 1% and 79%," Glantz wrote in a blog post. "The important point is that it does not include zero (i.e., no effect), so we can be confident that the drop was more than a chance finding."[56] One percent, seventy-nine percent, who cares, say the sizeless scientists of tobacco control. As long as the observed effect isn't zero, they will claim that science justifies their political interventions. This is no way to live, and it's no way to practice good science, either.

The opposite error of the sizeless stare is to exaggerate harms by multiplying very low and uncertain risks across entire populations. Even minuscule risks to an individual can seem substantial if multiplied across hundreds of millions of people. Such figures obscure vast uncertainties in epidemiology, providing a veneer of precision to what are in reality very rough estimates. A prime offender is the Centers for Disease Control and Prevention, which currently asserts that there are 41,000 deaths attributable to secondhand smoke in the United States each year.[57] If true, secondhand smoke is a bigger killer than guns or cars. Journalists repeat this figure without question. Yet here, too, some skepticism of the alleged crisis is in order.

As explained in the previous chapter, there is no direct way to count deaths caused by smoking. Unlike deaths due to gunshots and car accidents, deaths attributable to smoking are not discrete events that can be tallied. Even for active smoking, which has been extensively studied for decades, researchers' mortality estimates for the United States vary by up to 100,000 deaths per year. If it's that difficult to figure out how many smokers are dying because of direct tobacco use, guessing how many people perish from secondhand smoke is even more problematic. It's much easier to measure active smoking than passive, and the risks associated with actual smoking are better established than the risks of environmental smoke exposure. Because of this, estimates of mortality attributable to the latter are extremely sensitive to researchers' assumptions.

The CDC divides its figure of 41,000 secondhand smoke deaths into those caused by lung cancer (about 7,000) and heart disease (about 34,000). We've already covered the uncertainty regarding lung cancer. Epidemiologists generally agree that heart disease is the greater danger, but the magnitude of the effect is even more uncertain. The range of estimates from respected health authorities is very wide, and they are often much lower than the CDC's. Researchers affiliated with the World Health Organization estimated that for the entire region encompassing the United States, Canada, and Cuba, there were about 600 annual deaths due to lung cancer caused by second-hand smoke and 12,600 due to heart disease.[58] That's a third of the CDC's estimates, and for a population covering three countries, not just the United States. It's also an estimate for 2004, when smoking bans were just beginning to become popular policies. In the time since then, smoke exposure has been reduced substantially.

Research published in 2013 by Brian Rostron, then at Berkeley and now at the Food and Drug Administration's Center for Tobacco Products, also suggests that the CDC's estimates are excessive. High mortality estimates tend to assume that the cardiac risks of secondhand smoke take effect at very low levels of exposure. Rostron, whose data draws on objective biomarkers rather than subjective self-reporting, found instead that elevated risks appeared only among nonsmokers with the highest levels of exposure. Rostron argues that unrealistic estimates of the harms associated with low and medium levels of exposure inflate the CDC's mortality estimates.[59]

Two important trends cast doubt on the CDC's high estimates for secondhand smoke mortality. One is that mortality from heart disease, the primary mechanism by which the CDC argues secondhand smoke kills nonsmokers, has been declining for years. As Rostron notes in another paper, "[deaths] from ischemic heart disease for persons aged 65 and over decreased from 201,000 in 2000 to 158,000 in 2007 for U.S. men, and from 233,000 in 2000 to 170,000 in 2007 for U.S. women."[60] The other trend is the spread of smoking bans. Comprehensive bans were a rarity in the 1990s, but began to spread throughout the United States in the 2000s. As of 2019, twenty-seven states have enacted comprehensive smoking bans and more than 1,500 cities and counties ban smoking in workplaces and restaurants or bars.[61] Biomarkers confirm that nonsmokers are now exposed to far less environmental tobacco smoke than they were in the recent past. Surveys comparing populations from 1988-1994 to 2005-2010 show substantial shifts from medium exposure to low. In the earlier period, only 35% of adult nonsmokers were in the low exposure group. In the latter period, nearly 80% of them were. The proportion of nonsmokers in the high-exposure group shrank considerably over the same time, from 11.5% to just 5.3%.[62]

Both of these trends suggest that mortality attributable to secondhand smoke should be falling substantially, yet estimates are surprisingly sticky. The CDC's current estimate of 41,000 is only a little less than the 2006 Surgeon General's estimate of nearly 50,000. And as far back as 1990 one could read in *The New York Times* that "Dr. Stanton A. Glantz of the University of California at San Francisco estimated that passive smoke killed 50,000 Americans a year, two-thirds of whom died of heart disease."[63] Taking the long view, one might suspect that the claim that secondhand smoke kills around 50,000 Americans each year is justified more by its political utility than by a firm grounding in epidemiology.

Nonetheless, alarmist statements from health authorities are reported without question by the press. Journalists repeat the mantra that there is no safe level of secondhand smoke exposure, helping to justify ever further expansions of smoking bans regardless of whether they target the exposures that actually matter. (If most of the relevant exposure is happening in private homes, for example, then bans in outdoor spaces would serve only to harass smokers without affecting health outcomes.) Both perspectives — the sizeless stare that demolishes the scale of risk and the dubious population-level estimates that unrealistically inflate it — mislead the public by failing to place the risks of secondhand smoke exposure in a context relevant to daily life.

Secondhand smoke, however, is only the beginning. The "no risk-free level" argument reached its absurd apogee with the new threat of "thirdhand smoke," a phantom danger that epitomizes the contemporary tobacco control movement's abuse of science and the media's willingness to abet the spread of alarmist fears.

Say anything

Anti-smoking activists thoroughly succeeded in stretching science to demonize secondhand smoke, but why stop there? Thirdhand smoke is an even scarier menace. Thirdhand smoke, *The New York Times* explained in 2009, is "the term being used to describe the invisible yet toxic brew of gases and particles clinging to smokers' hair and clothing, not to mention cushions and carpeting, that lingers long after second-hand smoke has cleared the room."[64]

One doctor quoted in the *New York Times* story warned that "there are carcinogens in this third-hand smoke, and they are a cancer risk for anybody of any age who comes into contact with them." Dr. Jonathan Winickoff, a pediatrician at the Dana-Farber/Harvard Medical Center whose work inspired the press coverage, told *Scientific American* that "smokers themselves are also contaminated... smokers actually emit toxins."[65] Winickoff's research didn't actually investigate the health effects of this residue; it was just a phone survey asking random people whether thirdhand smoke concerned them.

The thirdhand smoke story resurfaced in 2011 when researchers unveiled a new study, again without examining exposure in humans. These researchers promoted the incredibly far-fetched conclusion that thirdhand smoke "is as damaging, and in some cases, more damaging than secondhand or firsthand smoke."[66] In addition to warning pregnant women and small children of these dangers, the authors concluded that the "same risk exists for adult workers who clean and change bed sheets in hotel rooms where cigarette smoking is allowed, all over the world: a problem of global proportions!"[67]

This reads like a parody of anti-smoking activism, but fear of thirdhand smoke was reported straight by prestigious newspapers. Less prestigious publications were even more blunt: "Don't smoke. Don't hang around smokers. And don't hang around people who hang around smokers," summarized *Vice* magazine.[68] Much of the coverage failed to mention that the first study was a phone survey, that later ones examined mouse or rat tissue rather than humans, or that there have yet to be any studies demonstrating that the residues left behind by tobacco smoke in real-world conditions are a substantial cause of illness. That hasn't stopped researchers from cautioning people against spending time in rooms where cigarettes might have been smoked decades ago. Dr. Neal Benowitz, head of the California Consortium on Thirdhand Smoke, told *National Geographic* that in "homes where we know no smoker has lived for 20 years, we've still found evidence of these compounds in dust, in wallboard." Dr. Georg Matt, another California-based researcher, warns that there is just no way to get rid of thirdhand smoke. "So far, we have not found an exposed environment where you cannot measure it any more. It's virtually impossible to remove this stuff unless you remove the flooring and drywall."[69] In another paper, researchers suggest that thirdhand smoke may pose a danger even in households where people use only oral tobacco, which does not emit smoke at all, on the basis that some tobacco-specific residues can nonetheless be detected in the dust.[70] This is the *reductio ad absurdum* of the sizeless stare: If it can be measured, it exists. And if it exists, it is extremely scary.

I don't know if studies will ever successfully demonstrate that thirdhand smoke increases the risk of any particular disease, and, crucially, neither do the researchers who have been promoting these fears to the public for more than a decade. I suspect that any risks that can be found will be minor and difficult to disentangle from other confounding factors, and that the funding for such research, totaling more than $7 million in California to date, could be better spent on more pressing health concerns.[71] Much like the investigations into secondhand smoke, the appeal of this research agenda is surely motivated in part by its political and social implications: Portraying thirdhand smoke as a cause of harm helps justify banning smoking in hotel rooms and apartments, barring smokers from fostering or adopting children, discriminating against smokers in employment, and intensifying the already significant stigma of being a smoker.

Fear of secondhand smoke alienated smokers by forcing them to step outside; fear of thirdhand smoke makes them untouchable pariahs. "My concern made me reluctant to let smokers hold my babies even though they refrained from smoking in my house," a columnist for *The Mirror* confessed without embarrassment.[72] Statements by thirdhand smoke researchers encourage this attitude. Jonathan Winickoff told the *New York Times* that "[the] stuff is so toxic that your brain is telling you: 'Get away.'"[73] Or to borrow the phrasing of Georg Matt in an interview with the *Huffington Post*, smokers are "mobile tobacco contamination packages."[74] What a way to regard one's fellow humans!

In her insightful 2016 book *Smokefree*, Australian anthropologist Simone Dennis finds a resonance between today's pseudoscientific fears of thirdhand smoke and pre-germ theory conceptions of "miasma," the belief that putrid air itself holds the capacity to cause disease:

Here, we are permitted the view of the air and its relationship with the body that circulated prior to Pasteur's paradigm-shifting discovery: bodies were subject to active air, and smell was not just an irritation, but instead illness in waiting. Smell was a physicality, just waiting for deposition into a body by way of the wind where, once deposited, it would grow into the maturity of illness.[75] [...] In the case of thirdhand smoke, the language of a witch-hunt is probably not too strong, if there exists smokers who can reach, as if by evil magic, into wombs to contaminate the unborn with their foul stench. And, certainly in the case of thirdhand smoke, we see plainly the corruption of values of trust, love, community, in the very purification techniques that exist to ensure the continuance of the community under such a threat.[76]

The thirdhand smoke scare exposes the extent to which the anti-smoking movement has abandoned scientific credibility. From pitching the Helena Miracle to journalists before peer review, to attacking anyone presenting contradictory evidence on the relationship of secondhand smoke to lung cancer, and finally to raising fears about the sinister presence of thirdhand smoke, prominent anti-tobacco researchers have adopted a thoroughly ends-justify-the-means approach to science. They will promote any finding that helps delegitimize tobacco use, no matter how far-fetched or unsupported by the evidence.

To their credit, a few figures in tobacco control are pushing back against this decline in scientific integrity. The most notable of these is Michael Siegel, a professor at the Boston University School of Public Health. An epidemiologist trained at the CDC, Siegel is no friend of the tobacco industry. For much of his career, his academic research and public activism made the case for indoor smoking bans. Around the turn of the century, however, he began to take issue with his colleagues' excess, publicly criticizing the anti-smoking movement's exaggerations and its efforts to ban smoking in outdoor spaces. As a result, Siegel has been banished from tobacco control email lists, falsely accused of taking money from Big Tobacco, and targeted by letters to his university demanding that he be fired. He laments that the anti-smoking movement has been taken over by ideology: "The current state of tobacco control I would describe, quite sadly, as misguided. It is now guided more by ideology and politics than by science."[77]

Ironically, Siegel suggests that the 1998 Master Settlement Agreement between big tobacco companies and state attorneys general is partially to blame for this state of affairs. The settlement required the companies to dismantle pro-industry organizations and to fund anti-smoking research. As a result, says Siegel, "The tobacco industry relinquished its watchdog role. Organizations in tobacco control used to be very careful because they knew the tobacco industry was watching and would call them on it if they exaggerated or distorted the truth. But after around 2000, the tobacco companies stopped playing this role and basically allow the tobacco control groups to say anything they want." He suggests that the infusion of money into the anti-smoking movement has allowed it to be hijacked by a few powerful groups that value political advocacy over sound science.[78]

This point is echoed by Geoffrey Kabat, the epidemiologist who was mercilessly attacked when his research in the *British Medical Journal* did not provide evidence linking secondhand smoke exposure to disease. "Owing to the increasing availability of ample funding from foundations such as the Robert Wood Johnson Foundation and voluntary organizations like the American Cancer Society, the California state tax-funded

Tobacco Related Disease Research Program, and especially the American Legacy Foundation... the field has grown enormously and become a veritable industry," he writes in his book *Hyping Health Risks*.[79] Kabat continues:

> It needs to be understood that in order to obtain funding in this area and justify how those funds are used, there is a powerful incentive to accept as a given the reigning consensus opinion on the health effects of passive smoking and a no less strong disincentive against drawing attention to the weaknesses or uncertainties in the underlying science. In the 1980s and earlier, before the rise of tobacco control as a field, it was almost exclusively epidemiologists who conducted studies of the health effects of tobacco exposure... They were true generalists. Tobacco was not their sole focus. In contrast, the new generation of tobacco control researchers included behavioral scientists, psychologists, health promotion specialists, and others, who, generally speaking, were more concerned with interventions to change behavior and with education and policy issues related to smoking.

The result of this dynamic is a scientific environment in which research is judged primarily for its usefulness in promoting the goals of tobacco control, dissent is punished by personal attacks, and dubious claims about the effects of second- and thirdhand smoke can be made with impunity, sure to receive favorable press coverage by reporters eager to write a shocking headline.

TOWARD BETTER TOBACCO JOURNALISM

When the Helena study and its successors were originally

published, a few scientists noted that the results were wildly implausible and the methodologies deeply flawed. So did a handful of journalists, most notably Jacob Sullum in the United States and Christopher Snowdon in England. Yet their criticism was generally ignored. Studies reporting miraculous declines in heart attacks made global headlines; when better studies came along contradicting those results, they barely registered as a blip in the media — too late to help smokers already banished from public life.

The claims made by tobacco control activists in recent years have become increasingly divorced from reality, yet the press tends to report them without critical scrutiny. A few journalists take their investigative role seriously, exposing the flaws and limitations of alarmist research. Most, however, approach the field with a lamentable credulousness, reporting without skepticism that smoking bans can decrease heart attacks by 60%, that secondhand smoke exposure is killing more Americans than guns or cars despite the exile of smokers from almost every public space, or that thirdhand smoke lingering on smokers' clothing will give us cancer.

The field of tobacco control is hardly alone in publishing dubious conclusions, although it is one of the worst offenders. To see why, it helps to view it through the lens of a paper published by John Ioannidis, the provocatively titled "Why Most Published Research Findings Are False."[80] In this widely cited paper, Ioannidis develops models to predict the circumstances most likely to foster the publication of false results. Many of them apply strikingly to anti-smoking research:

The smaller the studies conducted in a scientific field, the less likely the findings are to be true. Studies with small sample sizes are more likely to generate false results. Studies with large samples, all else equal, are more reliable. The "heart miracles" initially observed in small cities and later contradicted by studies of larger populations are a perfect example of this corollary in action, as are some of the studies linking second-hand smoke to lung cancer. Larger studies rarely support the headline-grabbing results of small outliers.

The smaller the effect size in a scientific field, the less likely the research findings are true. Strong effects are more reliably detected than weak effects. The impact of cigarette smoking on lung cancer is a strong effect and it is indisputably real. The effects of secondhand smoke on lung cancer are weak, with estimates of relative risk an order of magnitude smaller. Studies finding associations at such low levels are more likely to be false or off the mark.

The greater the flexibility in designs, definitions, outcomes, and analytical modes in a scientific field, the less likely the research findings are to be true. Flexibility makes it easier for bias to skew the results of a study. Meta-analyses of secondhand smoke research are vulnerable to bias by arbitrarily excluding contrary evidence or giving it lesser weight than more favorable results. Mortality estimates such as those from the CDC are highly sensitive to initial assumptions. Studies with great flexibility and little transparency can be biased, even unintentionally, in ways that lead to publishing false results.

The greater the financial and other interests and prejudices in a scientific field, the less likely the research findings are to be true. Much of the funding for tobacco research comes from ideologically motivated anti-smoking groups, and the fervor of the anti-smoking movement shapes both the research agenda and the interpretation of ambiguous evidence.

Of course, many of these arguments can be deployed with even greater force against research supported by the tobacco industry. But in years past, criticism from the industry helped enforce rigor in anti-smoking research in much the same way that the adversarial process in a courtroom trial forces both sides to justify their claims with evidence. Today that balance has been disrupted and the sources of bias outlined above have an unchecked impact on the quality of science. This lack of balance has important implications for health journalism. In the past, journalists reporting on a study released by one side knew exactly whom to contact for a critical counterpoint. Today, they rarely bother to probe anti-smoking studies for weaknesses or to seek comment from opposing parties. Good science journalism demands more than just regurgitating a scary-sounding number. It requires understanding the motivation and reliability of sources and speaking to critics to see if there's a counterargument they failed to mention. Reporters know to be skeptical of tobacco companies. Operating on an outdated mental model, they haven't yet learned to be skeptical of the tobacco control industry, too. It's long past time that they do.

None of this is to say that long-term exposure to second-hand smoke is without risk, that the shift in norms toward smoke-free spaces is not a good thing, or that science itself cannot be trusted. The weight of the evidence, as well as emerging research on the effects of particulate matter air pollution,[81] confirms that limiting smoke exposure is beneficial for health. But it's important to differentiate between the modest risks that have been identified in multiple high-quality studies and the alarmist claims made by the most ideologically-motivated researchers. It's no denial of science to conclude that many of the allegations made against second- and thirdhand smoke have been exaggerated to achieve political ends and stigmatize the act of smoking. Health and science writers should provide readers with the context they need to make sense of a potentially alarming study so that they can know, for example, whether a friend's smoky-smelling jacket is an annoyance to be tolerated or a biohazard to be forcibly evicted. Today's health reporters rarely make the effort, distorting public perception with unrealistic dangers. These fears have paved the way for a proliferation of intrusive regulations. The next chapter looks at some of these extreme measures, questions whether they are justified, and suggests ways that the interests of smokers and nonsmokers can be brought into a fairer balance.

ROOMS OF THEIR OWN

The freedom to smoke ought to be understood as a significant token of the class of freedoms, and when it is threatened one should look instantly for what other controls are being tightened, for what other checks on freedom are being administered. The attitude of a society toward the freedom to smoke is a test of the way it understands the rights of people at large, for at any time, all the time, a quarter to a half of all the adults in the world are puffing away at cigarettes.
— Richard Klein, *Cigarettes are Sublime*[1]

OF ALL THE places my writing has been posted over the years, the one I'm most proud of is the bulletin board outside the men's bathroom at the Horse Brass Pub in Portland, Oregon.[2] It's true that it's not the most prestigious honor in American letters, and my photograph accompanying the article was quickly graffitied with ridiculous facial hair and derogatory hand-scrawled commentary. Among beer drinkers in the Pacific Northwest, however, the Horse Brass is a legendary place. That legend arose thanks to the bar's former owner, Don

Younger, who took it over in 1976 and helped usher in the birth of craft beer in Oregon. The first time I saw a photo of Don, he was staring intently out of the pages of *Imbibe* magazine, his long gray hair spilling over his shoulders, his eyes bright, a wry smile beneath his beard and mustache. In one hand he held a half-empty pint of ale; in the other, what looks to be a lit cigarette.[3]

The first time I saw Don in person he was holding court at the pub in much the same pose. In 2008 I had moved across the country from Arlington, Virginia, arriving in Portland with no job and few friends. The Horse Brass lived up to its reputation for having the best beer selection in town as well as the smokiest interior. Cigarette smoke wafted through the place — it is rumored that the walls once gleamed white rather than their current shade of tan — and a crowd of cigar smokers reliably gathered at one end of the bar. As a stranger in town, the Horse Brass was the most convivial place I knew. On any given night I could show up alone, order a pint, light up a cigar, and soon be drawn into friendly conversation with the regulars. Don himself would often take the initiative of bringing guests together. "You don't come to a bar to read a book," I remember him growling to a patron who was reading at the bar one night. The young man was soon drawn into the community, charmed by Don, as people meeting him inevitably were.

Unfortunately, my enjoyment of the Horse Brass as a sanctuary for smokers was short-lived. I'd arrived in October and a new statewide smoking ban loomed on the new year. Don was the ban's most outspoken opponent. I'd welcomed myself to town by penning an op-ed against it in our local newspaper, and it was that clipping I found tacked to the wall outside the lavatory.[4] I introduced myself to Don as the writer of the piece, and our one and only conversation centered on the smoking ban and the futility of fighting it. It wasn't about the business, he told me. He knew there would still be plenty of people flocking to the Horse Brass after the ban, perhaps even more than there were before it. But he also knew that his bar would fundamentally change, and he felt that the pub culture he'd cultivated for three decades was being forcibly ripped away from him. "The heart and soul is being removed, surgically," he said in an interview with a local paper. "The state of Oregon runs my business now."[5]

A few days before the ban took effect, he and a bunch of regulars staged a photo called "The Last Smoker" with the group gathered in a rowdy row on a long table mimicking da Vinci's "Last Supper." Don sat at the center, his wiry frame and long hair suited to the place of an older, notably less ascetic Christ. Everyone was smiling.[6]

On New Year's Eve, just hours before the ban took force, regulars packed the Horse Brass to enjoy one last smoke. One patron I met that night, an immigrant from Germany, felt compelled to visit because the Horse Brass reminded him of the neighborhood bars he knew back home. "There's a place where the nanny has no place, and it's called a pub," he told me. Another woman said that we were gathered in the best bar in the world. "It will still be here," she sighed, "but it won't be the same."

At the stroke of midnight, we still had our cigarettes and cigars lit. "Put those out, they're illegal now!" one patron sarcastically admonished. No petty official was enforcing the ban yet, but from that moment on, violations could bring on fines of $500 per day and the ominous threat of "further administrative action." We puffed away in open rebellion, but Don was conspicuous by his absence, an exile from his own bar.

Don Younger died three years later. An inveterate smoker

and drinker, he was no one's bet to join the centenarian club. Nonetheless, those closest to him marked the smoking ban as the beginning of the end. "I think that killed Don," recalled fellow bar owner Lisa Morrison in an oral history of the Horse Brass published in *Willamette Week*. "He was heartbroken. He wanted to have his bar his way. I mean, he was not a healthy person, but I think that pushed him down a rabbit hole. He lost his spirit and his energy, and I think that had a lot to do with it." His close friend Carl Singmaster, whom I'd come to know over a few cigar nights at the Horse Brass, agreed. "You couldn't talk to him for more than five minutes without it coming up. He never let that go. It changed him and it changed his whole attitude; his whole trajectory just declined after that."[7]

For many, smoking bans are a welcome development. Nonsmoking beer lovers continue to visit the Horse Brass and happily arrive back home unscented by tobacco. But to many of us — whether publican, patron, or employee — these bans are violations of our rights as consenting adults and destructive of communities we've come to love. The Horse Brass is still a lively bar, but there's no doubt that the feeling of the place has been altered. Similar stories could be told of countless bars, cafes, and smoking lounges around the world, not to mention the businesses that closed entirely when smoking bans were imposed.

Advocates of smoking bans argue that this is the necessary price we pay for protecting people from secondhand smoke. Once a California oddity, such bans are now the norm, and they are getting ever wider in their scope. But this political victory comes with costs. One is the coercion of flesh-and-blood people like Don Younger and the forceful demolition of the communities they've nurtured. Another is basic respect for smokers themselves. By any realistic assessment of the health risks, today's smoking bans go far beyond the stated aim of protecting unwilling bystanders from harm. The burden of these policies falls almost entirely on people who smoke, an increasingly put-upon and invisible minority of the population. Their preferences are deemed unworthy of consideration, they are denied venues in which to take pleasure in each other's company, and they are looked down upon as helpless addicts and reviled as toxic outcasts.

EVERY SPACE IS CLAIMED

The American city that can lay claim to having the nation's strictest smoking ban changes every few years, though it's usually a progressive enclave in the state of California. A recent contender is Coronado, a resort town near San Diego, which in 2014 banned smoking on all public property, including streets, alleys, sidewalks, parkways, pathways, highways, and parking lots.[8] Similar outdoor smoking bans have spread throughout the United States and abroad. According to databases maintained by Americans for Nonsmokers' Rights, nearly 3,800 jurisdictions in the United States restrict outdoor smoking.[9] More than 300 municipalities ban smoking on beaches,[10] 1,500 ban it in parks,[11] and 500 have smoke-free outdoor dining laws.[12] An additional 2,375 American colleges and universities ban smoking throughout their campuses.[13]

The expansion of smoking bans to outdoor areas is a classic example of mission creep. The stated aim of early smoking bans was to protect nonsmokers, particularly workers, from chronic exposure to secondhand smoke. But when indoor smoking bans were enacted, anti-smoking groups did not declare victory and move on to other causes. Instead they continue to agitate for even further restrictions, from indoors to out. These extended bans cannot be justified by the same rationale; they are plainly motivated by the desire to control behavior and stigmatize smoking.

"We must be prepared to fight the aesthetics and personal standards argument as well as the health argument," one Australian anti-smoking activist wrote. "We should not underestimate the public awareness value of having smokers found guilty of negligent actions in all situations indoors and outdoors."[14] Smoking bans have always been rooted in delegitimization. As Stanton Glantz wrote approvingly back in 1987, bans discourage smoking "by implicitly defining smoking as an antisocial act."[15]

When New York City banned smoking at parks and beaches in 2010, the justification shifted explicitly from secondhand smoke to concerns about the mere sight of people smoking. One leading activist casually dismissed smokers' enjoyment of outdoor spaces as unworthy of consideration, declaring that there "is no redeeming value in smoking at beaches or parks."[16] The city's commissioner of health, Dr. Thomas Farley, argued that "families should be able to bring their children to parks and beaches knowing that they won't see others smoking... We will look back on this time and say 'How could we have ever tolerated smoking in a park?'"[17] The more that people like Farley use the coercive power of government to impose their moral code, the less that smoking is tolerated anywhere. Though progressive advocates of smoking bans would likely bristle at the comparison, they increasingly bring to mind Judge Robert Bork's defense of laws forbidding certain sexual behaviors: "Knowledge that an activity is taking place is a harm to those who find it profoundly immoral."[18]

Advocates of ever-expanding bans portray themselves as allies of smokers who encourage them to quit by tearing away social support for tobacco use, but rarely does anyone bother to ask smokers themselves how they feel about all of this. A perceptive exception is a paper published in the journal *Sociology of Health and Illness* by lead author Kirsten Bell, an anthropologist then at the University of British Columbia. Bell and her co-authors note that most tobacco research ignores the perspective of actual smokers and that the lack of interest in their experiences "speaks to the ways in which tobacco research is increasingly expected to further the goals of tobacco control."[19]

Evocatively titled "Every Space is Claimed," Bell's paper stands out for the empathy with which she and her co-authors approach the topic. They interviewed a diverse selection of smokers in Vancouver to better understand how smoking restrictions affect them. One consistent theme to emerge is that smokers find their habit viewed on a par with illicit drug use, as in this exchange with Mark, a man in his mid-forties:

> Mark: I would never go to somebody's house and
> ask them if I could smoke, put it that way. I
> wouldn't even put them in the position.
> LM: It's so automatic, and if you ask that they
> would go—.
> Mark: 'Can I go in your bathroom and smoke
> crack?'
> LM: Wow, it's up there, hey?
> Mark: It seems like that to some people, oh yeah,
> yeah, I think so, yeah, I think so.

Smokers reported feeling that their status as humans with equal dignity was doubted. Bob, a man in his fifties, explained, "Even if you can't articulate it you probably intuitively feel it in the same way that if you're black or a woman and you're being discriminated against, like even if you can't articulate it or you certainly can't prove it or you'd be at the Human Rights Commission, but you kind of know it's happening." Aisha, a woman in her twenties, noted that she had been forbidden from boarding buses after being seen smoking:

> Aisha: Like, I have had bus drivers not let me on the bus.
> LM: Why?
> Aisha: Because I was smoking at a bus stop. Open, not even covered, like.
> LM: Wow.
> Aisha: Open, nobody around me. There isn't like a three-year-old child next to me, and I'm not breathing smoke in their face or anything, and by myself smoking and they like won't let me on. They haven't let me on the bus.
> LM: What do they say? What could their rationale be?
> Aisha: That you're not allowed to smoke at a bus stop. And I say 'Fuck, I'm not'. That's not true at all... [R]ight now you're not allowed to smoke at a bus stop that's covered, under the cover, the rationale being that other people want to huddle under the cover, especially when it's raining and that's the way it's supposed to be, and that's fine. But a bus stop that's literally like a post in the street — fuck you! I can smoke here all I want!

To many anti-smoking advocates, stigmatizing people like

Mark, Bob, and Aisha is useful if it encourages them to quit. Bell and her co-authors are skeptical, noting that stigmatization could lead instead to feelings of powerlessness. They conclude:

> Participants in our study highlighted the growing restrictions on their ability to smoke and several explicitly recognised that legislative measures went well beyond the goal of protecting non-smokers from exposure to the effects of secondhand smoke and that the right to smoke altogether was being steadily eroded. Thus, while many participants expressed the view that smoking restrictions themselves were not intrinsically problematic, they emphasised that tobacco denormalisation had created an environment in which every public space was "claimed" by non-smokers, making it impossible to smoke in public at all without receiving judgement. Importantly, while study participants expressed considerable felt stigma in relation to their smoking, they also recounted numerous instances of overt censure and discrimination.
>
> Smokers' experiences in Vancouver raise important questions about the value and ethics of denormalisation strategies. Should a liberal state ever be complicit in shaming its citizens?

Targets of this shaming tend be among society's least well off. Smokers now comprise only about 15% of the American population, and they are clustered among those with lower incomes and less education. More than 20% of adults without a high school degree smoke cigarettes, compared to 7% of college graduates and 4% of adults with a graduate degree.[20] Thus, when policymakers banish smokers from public places, they are increasingly banishing the poor and uneducated. No wonder smoking bans are popular.

As the boundaries of these bans expand into outdoor spaces, some advocates for the poor have stepped up to oppose them. When Seattle proposed banning smoking in public parks, the American Civil Liberties Union of Washington objected. "The rule would disproportionately impact the poor and homeless, who do not have living rooms and front porches, with minimal health benefits over the current rule," it argued. "If individuals had a private residence to smoke in, there would be less of a need to smoke in a public park. Banning low-income and homeless individuals from public spaces simply for smoking is not an acceptable approach."[21]

Class issues have always been implicit in smoking ban debates, but occasionally the mask slips and they are made explicit. In Eugene, Oregon, for example, a proposal to ban smoking (and dogs!) in the entirety of downtown was aimed specifically at ridding the area of loiterers who were perceived as being bad for business.[22] A similar proposal was backed by real estate developers in Providence, Rhode Island. "[A] smoke-free downtown is more than a public-health issue," they argued. "It's also an economic-development issue because it would improve the quality of life downtown, making the area better for development."[23] Outdoor smoking bans sanitize cities not by making them healthier, but by ridding them of undesirable people.

"I recently saw a woman brandishing the Mercedes Benz of strollers walk through a sea of idling traffic toward a smoker only to say the smoker was 'murdering her baby' by polluting the air," wrote June Thunderstorm in a recent essay for the left-wing magazine *The Baffler*.[24] Thunderstorm decried how smoking restrictions affect blue collar workers: "Such an act has nothing to do with protecting children, and everything to do with venting bourgeois malaise by attacking powerless people whom state authorities have constructed as abject and undeserving of respect," she wrote. "Whether because workers smoke or their friends do, the traditional places of working-class congregation are now closed to them — the pub, the diner, the park, and even the sidewalk. It is no coincidence that fifteen feet from the door stands the gutter."

Anthropologist Simone Dennis noted a similar class dynamic in her decade of observing smoking behavior in Australia, remarking that the result of seeking purity in smoke-free spaces is a dirty remainder of smokers at the fringes:

Already, in the realm of space, smokers constitute a source of class contamination, as they sully the air — an increasingly odourless middle class air — with smoky evidence of their class. They equally contaminate the temporal register, making 'zero smoking' much like 'zero unemployment' — a striven for time sullied by the contaminating, stubborn continuance of an abject class.[25]

Smoking bans are primarily the product of the progressive left, but plenty of politicians on the right are equally happy to police this behavior. Mitt Romney signed the Massachusetts ban into law,[26] and then-presidential candidate Mike Huckabee floated the idea of a federal ban after proudly enacting a statewide one in Arkansas.[27] Anti-smoker sentiment is thoroughly bipartisan, but opposition to further restrictions cuts against simple divides of left and right. (Libertarians, bless them, have opposed smoking bans from the beginning.)

In 2018, three articles about smoking bans appearing within the same month caught my attention. In the first, *The New York Times* documented the surprising victory of Austria's far-right

Freedom Party in overturning an impending smoking ban. "Austria's far right wants the freedom to smoke," reads the headline. Though willing to embrace authoritarianism when it suits their interests, the party harnessed antipathy to political correctness and affection for Viennese cafe culture to wage a campaign premised on freedom of choice. Its leaders succeeded in preserving smoking options for small businesses throughout the country.[28]

The second article was an interview in *Slate* with left-leaning journalist Barbara Ehrenreich in which she described smoking bans as "a war on the working class" that takes away the few places that remain for workers to get together and take comfort from their jobs. "It's very tragic when I see employees gathered outside a workplace like a big-box store or an office building trying to smoke in the wind and the rain because that's the only place they can go," she said.[29] Neither the *New York Times* reporter nor the *Slate* interviewer seem to know quite what to make of the situation. Who, they seem to be asking, could possibly be against a smoking ban in 2018? All the right-thinking people are in favor. Yet the issue has somehow united American civil libertarians, the Freedom Party of Austria, and Barbara Ehrenreich in opposition.

The third article, in *The New York Daily News*, describes the sort of petty legal harassment of smokers that brings these unexpected allies together. It covered a bill introduced by New York City Councilman Peter Koo that would have made it illegal to smoke a cigarette and walk at the same time. Under Koo's proposal, anyone caught doing so would be subject to a $50 fine. (Smoking while stationary would still be permitted; smokers would only be fined if they dared to get some exercise while in the act.) Having already kicked smokers out of work-places, restaurants, bars, and parks, Koo was indignant to occasionally find himself behind a smoker on the sidewalk. "In a perfect world, every smoker would have the self-awareness to realize smoking while walking subjects everyone behind you to the fumes," he said.[30] In the real world — a world in which smokers have nowhere left to go, in which minorities are subject to the indignity of stop-and-frisk, in which New York cops might choke a man to death on suspicion of selling individual cigarettes — politicians might recognize that giving police yet another reason to harass innocent people on the street may produce outcomes worse than enduring brief exposure to secondhand smoke.

If opposition to smoking bans becomes the domain of libertarians, the far right, and the far left, it will be because so-called liberals — using the broad meaning of the term to indicate a political philosophy that values liberty — have failed to live up to their name. There are scant places remaining where smokers can light up in peace, especially if they are poor. But as we'll see, the laws do tend to make accommodation for the rich.

ROOMS FOR ME, BUT NOT FOR THEE

For most of today's smokers, the feeling that "every space is claimed" is justified. If they're financially well-off, however, they can probably find a smoke-filled room in which to gather. In Oregon, I can no longer light up at Don Younger's Horse Brass, where cigarette and cigar smokers once sat elbow-to-elbow with pints of ale, but I can frequent a fancy downtown steakhouse called El Gaucho that operates one of the few cigar lounges grandfathered in under our statewide smoking ban. Cigarette smoking is illegal in these lounges, but cigars are permitted. The rules governing exceptions are arbitrary: Cigar bars must be able to show tobacco sales records from 2006 (meaning no new ones can open), cannot have more than forty seats, must be licensed to sell liquor (not just beer and wine), cannot allow lottery games (too blue collar), and are required to have a humidor on premise (how fancy!). The law says, in essence, that you're allowed to smoke inside, but only if you're classy about it.[31]

Grandfather clauses like the one in Oregon are common and accomplish three goals simultaneously: They keep wealthier cigar smokers happy, allow a few existing businesses to continue catering to smokers, and ensure that those businesses are protected from future competition. By doing so they buy off some of the most vocal opposition to smoking bans, depriving people like Don Younger of potential allies while siphoning away his cigar-smoking clientele.

When smoking bans do allow for exceptions, they tend to go to politically influential groups. Casinos and racetracks are the best examples. Closely intertwined with politics, the taxes they deliver give lawmakers a stake in any revenue that would be lost under a smoking ban. Research by the Federal Reserve Bank of St. Louis concluded that Illinois casinos saw revenue decline by about 20% after smoking was prohibited, resulting in an estimated $200 million reduction in tax revenue.[32] Legislators are wary of similar declines, especially when they border states with more libertine rules. As a result, owners of gambling businesses are among the most successful at securing exemptions.

The ultimate form of self-dealing, however, is when lawmakers ban smoking for everyone except themselves. In St. Louis, Missouri, local politicians notoriously refused to follow the same rules they laid down for ordinary citizens, continuing to smoke in an exclusive, invitation-only athletic club. "The club, known as the MAC, has flouted the law since it was enacted Jan. 1, 2011, openly leaving ashtrays in the lounge, hosting hazy boxing matches and allowing men in suits to gather weekly at the bar with tumblers in one hand, cigars in the other," the *St. Louis Post-Dispatch* reported in 2012. "The city cited and fined the club twice. The citations ended up in municipal court, where attorneys began working out a deal." The city's health director eventually declared the club a "special entity" and allowed its wealthy, politically influential members to continue lighting up indoors. Other bar owners in St. Louis, forced to kick out their smoking patrons, were given no such courtesy.

In Washington, DC, city councilman Jack Evans secured similar special treatment for the Friendly Sons of Saint Patrick annual gala and a charitable boxing night. Evans had voted in favor of the District's smoking ban, but when he realized that it would extinguish smoking at his favorite parties, he objected that "to eliminate cigars would be ludicrous."[33] In 2011, he successfully wrote a special exemption into law.[34] Charities in DC that don't happen to have a city councilman among their members have no such luck.

There's also Coronado, California, the resort town that made national headlines for enacting one of the country's most stringent smoking bans. Even it allows for a few exceptions, most notably on the city-operated golf course. "In full disclosure," confessed the mayor, who supported banning smoking in other outdoor locations, "I golf and do occasionally have a cigar while golfing. Maybe that influenced my decision."[35]

Smoking restrictions also tend to discriminate against minorities, allowing high-end cigar bars to stay open while forbidding hookah lounges that typically cater to people of Middle Eastern descent. In 2009, the owner of a hookah bar in North Carolina complained that the state's new smoking ban "basically protected the playground of the rich and elite" by forcing his business to close while cigar bars remained open.[36] He was absolutely right: There is no reason other than prejudice for allowing cigar bars while banning hookah lounges, a distinction that hinges more on the racial and class profile of the consumers than on the health risks of secondhand smoke.

As smoking bans have expanded to encompass both indoor and outdoor spaces, one of the last refuges smokers can claim is the private home. Here, too, the financially well-off are at an obvious advantage. Renters are at the mercy of landlords and many apartment buildings now forbid smoking both indoors and in outdoor common areas. Some jurisdictions ban smoking in apartment buildings and attached homes. These days, if a person wants a place in which to leisurely enjoy a smoke, it helps to be able to afford a freestanding house.

This disparity came into focus in 2015 when the Department of Health and Human Services announced a new policy banning smoking in public housing. How to balance the desires of smokers and nonsmokers in public housing is a complicated issue. On the one hand, residents of private apartment buildings have shown a preference for properties that don't allow indoor smoking, and it would be unfair to deny residents of public housing the same option. On the other hand, these residents are often elderly, poor, handicapped, or addicted. Enforcing a ban on recalcitrant smokers risks targeting some of the most vulnerable members of society with cruel eviction.[37]

This is obviously not a dilemma faced by people who own their houses, and a compassionate person might wonder whether there are policies short of a universal ban that would better accommodate the needs of public housing residents. A more authoritarian approach would be to strip away the freedom to smoke from everyone, including private homeowners. This was the solution favored by writers at the website Vox. "One major problem with this policy is it seems to single out low-income people for a problem that is universal — second-hand smoke can kill anyone who's around it," wrote reporter German Lopez. "But there's an easy solution to that: Indoor smoking should be banned *everywhere* — inside bars, restaurants, your home. Full stop."[38] Lopez's colleague Dylan Matthews agreed. "Banning smoking indoors outright — regardless of whether you own your house or rent or get public assistance — isn't in the cards right now," he lamented. "When restrictions apply to people outside of public housing, freakouts tend to ensue. But it'd be a far fairer way to save lives and prevent secondhand smoke than a ban that's only limited to public housing residents."[39]

It's not clear how the writers believe such a ban would be enforced — snitching neighbors, cops conducting no-knock raids looking for ashtrays on the kitchen table? — but telling consenting adults what they can do with legal products in the confines of their own homes would be a legitimate reason to freak out. And if this idea ever does get passed into law, it's safe to assume that, as with other drug laws, the least well-off will suffer the brunt of enforcement.

The writers at Vox deserve a perverse sort of credit for gliding down the slippery slope that smoking ban opponents have long warned against, but the rest of us are under no obligation to go along with them. Having acknowledged that smoking bans disproportionately restrict the poor, the desire for equality should not require comparable intrusions targeting the rich. We should ask instead whether our current policies are consistent with the demands of liberalism and whether nonsmokers are failing to treat their fellow citizens as equals.

· · ·

UNPACKING MILL'S HARM PRINCIPLE

As noted in the previous chapter, smoking ban debates are typically framed as being primarily about public health and epidemiology. If research shows that secondhand smoke is harmful, say ban advocates, then it follows that restrictions are justified. This argument is convenient for anti-smoking activists and for the currently fashionable mode of explanatory journalism, both of which assume that any negative impact on health whatsoever proves the need for legislative intervention. "There is a health effect, so there ought to be a law," say the researchers. "Science says smoking bans work," echo the journalists.

That leap from epidemiology to law elides thornier points of disagreement. To treat the debate over smoking bans as entirely a question of science is to make a basic category error. Science can and should inform the debate, but it's incapable of settling it. The question is ultimately one of political philosophy: of whose rights matter, and of how people with different preferences can get along.

The classic statement of when, in a liberal society, citizens are justified in forcibly restricting a person's actions was put forward by John Stuart Mill in *On Liberty*. The short answer: to prevent harm to others. A person's "own good, either physical or moral, is not a sufficient warrant," Mill continued. "He cannot rightfully be compelled to do or forbear because it will be better for him to do so, because it will make him happier, because, in the opinion of others, to do so would be wise, or even right."[40]

Adherence to this limit on government action is often more aspirational than real, but it's still a useful framework for evaluating smoking bans. Does it settle the question of where one may smoke? Alas, that's not so easy. Opponents and advocates alike tend to read their preferred outcome into Mill's harm principle. Under the classical liberal or libertarian interpretation, smoking bans impede the free choices of adults. No one is forced to spend time in a business that allows smoking. The owner chooses what to allow on his or her property, employees choose to work there, and customers choose to patronize it. No one is exposed without consent. If consumers demand smoke-free businesses, the market will provide them. Government should stay out of it.

In contrast, ban advocates contend that smoking restrictions are justified by the harm principle. People have the right to breathe clean air. Workers, in particular, have the right to not be exposed to toxic substances as part of their jobs. Smokers infringe these rights by fouling the air that people around them must breathe. In economic terms, smokers create a negative externality, imposing the costs of their behavior onto unwilling and uncompensated others. The market won't correct this, so the government must step in.

Judging by the political success of smoking bans, the libertarian argument is clearly unsatisfactory for most voters. And while my sympathies lie with that interpretation, it's admittedly hard to fathom the degree to which smokers were once able to foist their preferences onto everyone else. Most anywhere one went, there were ashtrays available and people lighting up. While it was technically true that nonsmokers weren't forced to go to most of those places, they often wanted for alternatives. For all intents and purposes, going through daily life entailed frequent exposure to other people's cigarette smoke. Matters of health aside, this was at the very least a nuisance, and even a smokers' rights advocate like myself can acknowledge that shifting norms against the presumption that people can light up anywhere they please are an improvement over the way things used to be.

Some restrictions on smoking in truly public places, such as courthouses and public school buildings, can be reasonably justified by the harm principle. So too, arguably, can those for common carriers like passenger trains and commercial airlines. It's a stretch, however, to extend this justification to bans in bars, restaurants, and similar venues. Although these are public places in the sense of being open to all comers, they are privately owned and operated. Guests choose whether or not to patronize them. If a nonsmoker walks into a business that clearly caters to smokers, he can't reasonably complain of being harmed against his will. If he then uses the power of the state to demand that everyone put out their smokes, he becomes the one violating the liberty of his fellow citizens.

The unquestioned assumption of many ban advocates is that exposure to secondhand smoke cannot be a choice. "[There's] a world of difference between risks we choose to accept in exchange for rewards we want — like driving a car, drinking alcohol, or having unprotected sex — and having those risks imposed upon us against our will," Naomi Oreskes and Erik Conway argue in their book *Merchants of Doubt*. "The second-hand smoke debate was crucial precisely because the risk wasn't a choice and wasn't natural. It was a man-made risk that was being imposed without consent."[41] This just begs the question of why no one can consent to socializing with smokers. It's perfectly possible to do so — I've done it myself many times! Smoking has always been a social activity, and to deny that adults can choose to enjoy it together, including nonsmokers among them, assumes the very thing it's ostensibly proving.

Smoking bans plainly infringe the liberties of consenting adults, so other anti-smoking activists have put forth more nuanced arguments. One is to say that bans correct for a market failure. This argument was never quite coherent, requiring one to simultaneously believe that there was massive unmet demand for smoke-free spaces and also that profit-seeking business owners refused to provide them. The hospitality business is unrelentingly competitive, so the motive for refusing to cater to the supposedly strongly held preferences of nonsmokers was left unexplained. Local anti-smoking groups often undercut their own argument by pointing out that hundreds of bars and restaurants in their cities had successfully transitioned to being smoke-free voluntarily, demonstrating that the change could be both consensual and profitable.[42]

In truth, smoking bans were most likely to pass in places that had populations primed to accept them,[43] and they accelerated trends toward smoke-free spaces that were already underway. To be sure, top-down bans helped shift norms against indoor smoking more decisively than a gradual transition would have, but they did so by imposing a one-size-fits-all solution that tramples on dissenting preferences. Contrary to the claims of advocates who dismissed worries of lost patronage at smoke-friendly businesses, this does have an economic impact. A comprehensive review published in 2014 concluded that while smoking bans have not substantially harmed the hospitality sector as a whole, gains and losses are not evenly distributed. Imposition of a ban was associated with a decline in sales for bars. The best economic performance was seen under partial bans that made room for some exceptions, most likely for the simple economic reason that they allowed smokers and nonsmokers alike to exercise their preferences.[44]

The stronger argument in favor of smoking bans was to shift the focus from patrons to employees. This relies on the intuition that doing one's job should not require exposing oneself to toxic substances. But even taking claims about the health effects of secondhand smoke at face value, it's difficult to justify a complete ban on offering hospitality to smokers. The most dangerous jobs in the United States involve fishing, logging, and driving, yet we find ways to balance those risks with commercial demand.[45] According to the Bureau of Labor Statistics, the fatality rate among fishing workers in recent years is consistently 30 to 50 times higher than the rate for workers overall.[46] These deaths are concentrated in certain fisheries, such as those seeking West Coast Dungeness crabs, where the fatality rate climbs up to more than 300 annual deaths per 100,000 full time workers — almost eighty times higher than the mortality rate for the average American worker.[47]

I have never heard anyone suggest banning the consumption of Dungeness crabs, although demand for them can be unequivocally linked to an extremely high rate of worker fatalities. Yet advocates of comprehensive smoking bans suggest that carrying a tray of drinks into a smoke-filled room is so perilous a task that no one may be permitted to do it for pay. If such a risk-averse standard were applied consistently, many more jobs would be put on the chopping block.

It is, to repeat, a good thing that expectations have shifted in favor of smoke-free spaces. When smoking was ubiquitous, it was reasonable to object that workers wanting to avoid it had few options available to them. It is undeniably a sign of progress that exposing oneself to secondhand smoke is no longer requisite for working in the hospitality industry. But it doesn't follow that no smoke-friendly businesses should be permitted to exist anywhere under any circumstances; no credible weighing of on-the-job dangers would identify providing hospitality to smokers as an occupation so uniquely deadly that it should be completely illegal. The push for 100% compliance with smoke-free legislation says more about society's low view of smokers than it does about the risks of secondhand smoke; it reflects a decision that the preferences of owners, employees, and patrons of smoke-friendly businesses simply do not count. (The extension of smoking bans to outdoor areas, where smoke is transient and employees may not even be present, is an even clearer demonstration that worker health is not the primary motivation for these laws.)

The simplistic interpretation of the harm principle favored by smoking ban advocates doesn't hold up to closer scrutiny; protecting workers is the polite fiction by which nonsmokers justify imposing their will on an unpopular minority, denying smokers access to a widening circle of public and semi-public spaces. Today's bans reach well beyond the boundaries needed to protect workers or secure smoke-free social venues. The continuing drive to eliminate the few places in which smoking is permitted is spurred on not so much by ordinary citizens as it is by the institutions of professional tobacco control. This movement is ideologically motivated and increasingly unburdened by any constraints respecting individual liberty.

Tobacco control and the pink police state

Having written about tobacco policy for more than a decade, I've found myself in countless conversations on the topic of smoking bans. When I ask people if they support these policies, nonsmokers (and many smokers) usually say yes. But when I follow up by asking if some businesses ought to be allowed to cater specifically to smokers, they usually say yes to that, too. In my experience, most people's views fall somewhere between pure *laissez faire* and the boundless paternalism of professional tobacco control. They have a pragmatic attitude grounded in a time in which smoking norms and regulations were vulnerable to change: a transition from having to opt-out of smoking spaces to having to opt-in to them.

As cigarettes rose in popularity throughout the first half of the twentieth century, smoking in many countries became permitted by default. If you didn't like it, that was your problem; the burden was on nonsmokers to find places that catered to their preference. By the 1970s, this was leading to an understandable backlash. Although it wasn't the first law of its kind, one could cite the passage of New York City's smoking ban in 2003 as an inflection point marking the transition to an opt-in smoking standard. As similar bans spread throughout the country, smoking became forbidden by default. "No smoking" signs have become superfluous; now we use signs to denote the places where one *can* smoke. Under the new norms, these places are highly circumscribed and people are only exposed to smoky environments if they choose to enter them. This shift is generally a good thing; a society with fewer places claimed by smokers is more enjoyable for many reasons, not just for health.

The challenge of transitioning to an opt-in standard, however, is that the freedom to opt-in has to actually be preserved. It's here that supposedly liberal defenders of smoking bans often fail to live up to their end of the bargain. They pay no attention to the nuances of smoking ban exemptions and take no notice when they are stripped away. Having come to feel entitled to nonsmoking spaces, they become less troubled claiming ever more of them. The expansion of smoking bans has proceeded by bait-and-switch: What began with the alleged motivation of protecting workers became a naked exercise of power, with nonsmokers coercively claiming every desirable space for themselves.

This expansion is driven by the researchers and activists in tobacco control for whom the limits of liberalism hold no sway. These are well-funded groups that lobby for new restrictions, grade states and cities on their policies, fund research friendly to their causes, and promote the most alarming claims about tobacco smoke regardless of their scientific merit, all with the ultimate aim of achieving complete abstinence. They are not committed to the kind of liberalism that generally restrains us from coercing our fellow citizens or interfering with consensual exchanges on private property. Under the creeping demands of contemporary public health, the liberal framework espoused in Mill's harm principle collapses.

Perhaps a better way to understand this is as a manifestation of the "pink police state," a fruitful description of contemporary politics coined by social commentator James Poulos. In Poulos's telling, the pink police state obliterates the public/private distinction that limits government action in classical liberal philosophy. The newly relevant divides are between health/sickness and safety/danger. This regulatory regime "pursues health and safety at the expense of liberty in the context of a culture that demands robust interpersonal freedom."[48] The pink police state protects some liberties while curtailing others, specifically those that the state identifies with sickness or danger. It's a shift that transcends partisan boundaries. Writes Poulos:

> The new regime is not totalitarian, fascist, socialist, capitalist, conservative, or liberal, according to the accepted and common definitions of those terms. It is not even adequately described as corporatist, although corporatism is very much at home within it. [... the pink police state] enforces the restrictions and *permissions* doled out by its sense of 'clean

living.' To invoke Michel Foucault again, ours is an age when governance is inseparable from hygiene in the minds of the elite that rules over both the private and public sector. To them, everything is theoretically a health issue.[49]

When health becomes the overriding concern, the state can insert itself into life without respect for public/private boundaries. Within the official realm it banishes that which threatens health and safety. The emphasis on hygiene is particularly insightful: Smokers do not merely engage in unhealthy behavior. They are themselves perceived as toxic and dirty; anything tobacco touches is deemed illegitimate in the official sphere.

Instead of respecting autonomy within private spaces, the pink police state as manifested by tobacco control authoritatively defines the purpose of those spaces to exclude tobacco use. Thus, a park is for healthy activities, not for smoking. A drug store is for medicine, not for selling cigarettes. A restaurant is for eating. A bar is for drinking. A sidewalk is for walking. Downtown is for shopping. No place is for lighting up tobacco. Smoke in your house, for now at least, until people lose the will to "freak out" when the state decides to tell them what their homes are for, too.

A few solitary voices in tobacco control have pushed back against this proliferation of ever more intrusive smoking bans. As early as 2000, *Tobacco Control* editor Simon Chapman criticized his peers' enthusiasm for outdoor restrictions:

Such proposals "push the envelope" of tobacco control into areas where questions need to be asked to ensure tobacco control policies are firmly anchored to scientific evidence and especially concern those who value the freedom of individuals to do what they please to the extent that this does not harm others. They invite consideration of whether zero tolerance of public exposure to toxic agents is a reasonable policy for civil societies and whether the loudly proclaimed exquisite sensitivities of a small minority should drive public policy.[50]

Michael Siegel, an advocate of strict indoor smoking bans, also draws the line at bans in open outdoor spaces. "My perception is that the reason smoking is being singled out is that there is some underlying hatred of smokers and a disrespect for their life choices, as well as for their right to make these choices," writes Siegel.[51] He notes that this is often a class issue. "Smokers have become a social class whose personal autonomy and behavior choices are not respected in the same way that we respect the autonomy and behavior choices of other groups, especially wealthier classes."[52]

For the time being, at least, the fight over smoking bans has been won decisively by paternalists. Reversion to 1960s smoking policies is a non-starter. But now that chronic exposure to secondhand smoke is, for most of us, a thing of the past, we can and should revisit the issue of how to accommodate smokers in a liberal society.

ROLLING BACK THE BANS

Earlier in this chapter I mentioned El Gaucho, the steakhouse that operates one of only six cigar bars legally permitted to serve the nearly 2.5 million people living in the Portland, Oregon, metropolitan area. That's not many to choose from, but cigar smokers here are better off than our neighbors to the north in Washington. That state has one of the strictest smoking bans in the country, allowing for no exceptions and banning smoking outdoors within twenty-five feet of doors and windows. When outdoor spaces are available at such a distance, the cold and rainy weather of the Pacific Northwest often makes them unsuitable for enjoying a quick cigarette, much less a long-burning cigar. Outside of their homes, residents of Washington have virtually no indoor spaces in which to smoke.

El Gaucho also has a location in Tacoma, Washington, and the owners believed renovations would allow them to serve cigar smokers in their existing smoking lounge. They spent $15,000 on a separate room that guests would access by passing through a twenty-five-foot passageway. To prevent employees from being exposed to smoke, the lounge was to be operated as a separate corporation staffed exclusively by its three owners. This was a lot of effort and expense just to provide a comfortable place to light up, but it wasn't enough to satisfy health inspectors, who ordered the lounge closed immediately after its opening.[53]

While this is an extreme example, it illustrates the boundlessness of contemporary smoking bans and the convoluted lengths business owners must go through to facilitate voluntary exchange among consenting adults. When the government can reach into a privately-owned smoking lounge protected by a twenty-five-foot passageway to tell smokers to stub out their cigars, one needn't be a card-carrying libertarian to feel that the nanny state has gotten out of hand. One can acknowledge this without concluding that smoking bans should be repealed entirely; there are plenty of moderate reforms that could better accommodate the rights of people who enjoy tobacco. If you, the reader, consider yourself a liberal in the broad sense — a person who values liberty and respects the rights of adults to be in control of their own bodies — then you should take seriously the idea that today's laws often fail to treat smokers as equal citizens.

Outdoor restrictions are the most obvious targets for reform. These bans have the least plausible claim to being about protecting the health of bystanders and are most clearly motivated by simple dislike of smoking or smokers. Contemporary ban advocates seek to insulate the public not just from potentially harmful levels of exposure, but from mere whiffs of smoke or just the sight of someone smoking. This does not befit a liberal society and these policies disproportionately affect the least well off. With some reasonable exceptions (children's playgrounds, for example), all-encompassing bans applying to beaches, parks, city sidewalks, college campuses, hospital grounds, prison yards, and the like should be curtailed or repealed.

Nonsmokers will be less enthusiastic about rolling back bans on bar and restaurant patios, but these should also be reconsidered. Where smoking on patios is legal, the option has likely helped to minimize the overall economic impact of smoking bans by allowing smokers to self-sort into places that can accommodate them. When this option is taken away, bar owners have complained of lost revenue. In jurisdictions that have forbidden outdoor smoking where food is served, for example, businesses sometimes choose to remove the food menus rather than the ashtrays — a textbook example of regulations having unintended consequences that leave consumers worse off.[54]

There is clearly demand for outdoor smoking areas, and given the minimal impacts of secondhand smoke in an open-air setting, there's no reason to disallow them. Of course, this means that nonsmokers would sometimes face a choice of sharing an outdoor space with smokers or taking their business elsewhere, but that's the cost of pluralism. They'd also find that many businesses would continue to voluntarily forbid outdoor smoking regardless of their legal options.

Proposals to relax indoor smoking bans will be met with the most resistance. Whenever I write in criticism of smoking bans, many online commenters inevitably react as if I were suggesting we go back to the bad old days of smoking on airplanes, in hospital waiting rooms, and in the aisles of super-markets. But smoking bans are not an all-or-nothing affair. Public policy takes place at the margins, and the margins now extend far beyond the goal of protecting people from high concentrations of secondhand smoke. Social norms and economic demand have shifted decisively against smoking in commercial venues. The ubiquity of cigarette smoking in the previous century was contingent on a multitude of factors that are unlikely to be repeated; business owners, employees, and consumers have come to expect and appreciate smoke-free spaces. The success that smoking bans have had changing norms weakens the need for keeping those laws on the books, at least in their strictest forms. Legislation is one way of governing where people may smoke, but it shouldn't be the only way; norms and consumer expectations dissuade many businesses from allowing smoking, even when they're legally permitted to do so.

Outside of professional tobacco control, most people I talk to agree that smoking bans should make some allowances for smoke-friendly venues. In practice, the laws that govern these exemptions are a mess. They are often arbitrary, monopolistic, and elitist. Grandfather clauses protect businesses from compe-tition, and high-end places like cigar bars are more likely to get a pass than hookah lounges or dive bars. States and cities should replace patchwork exemptions with an open process based on objective criteria such as the size of venue, ventilation requirements, and age restrictions. The type of tobacco enjoyed in those spaces should have no bearing on their ability to operate, putting cigarettes, cigars, pipes, hookah, and other products on equal footing.

English-speaking countries and much of Europe have implemented comprehensive bans that leave very few options for smokers. For a more tolerant approach, we can look to Berlin. Bars in Berlin are allowed to have separate smoking areas. An entire bar can be smoke-friendly if it is smaller than seventy-five square meters in size, has only one room, does not serve hot food, and forbids minors. As a result, smoking is permitted in many more bars in Berlin than elsewhere, which is frustrating for nonsmoking visitors and some Berliners, but the city's devotion to respecting choice is commendable. Even so, an increasing number of bars in Berlin are responding to demand for smoke-free spaces by forbidding smoking voluntarily. As a press officer for the city's health department stated recently, "The point of laws is to balance the interests of the public, and there's a good balance now."[55] What a refreshingly tolerant perspective!

As much as I enjoy my visits to Berlin, I suspect that most jurisdictions in the United States aren't ready to accept that level of permissiveness. Policymakers here will likely insist on greater control over smoke-friendly venues. Yet we have many examples of "undesirable" businesses that are allowed to operate under varying degrees of regulation. Alcohol and cannabis provide two potential models. States and cities balance commercial demand for these with safety and other concerns, limiting their number via licensing. A transparent and accessible licensing process for smoke-friendly bars and smoking lounges could limit the number in operation, enforce compliance with regulations, and raise revenue for state and local governments.

Anti-smoking activists will, of course, absolutely reject any proposal to weaken smoking bans. They long ago abandoned the pretense that these laws are justified by the need to protect bystanders. They wish to coercively remove the scent and sight of anyone smoking in public. They are free to advocate for that, but we should recognize professional anti-smoking activism for what it has become: a contemporary manifestation of the old-time temperance movement, wrapped in the modern clothing of epidemiology but with the same tired contempt for individual liberty.

When smoking restrictions were first imposed on airplanes, advocates dismissed libertarian warnings of a slippery slope. Every step of the way, they have assured us that they were only taking reasonable measures to protect nonsmokers and that individual freedom would be preserved. Thirty years later, smokers have been booted from restaurants, bars, patios, college campuses, beaches, golf courses, sidewalks, parking lots, hospital grounds, solitary park benches, and even from their homes. It turns out the slope was pretty damn slippery after all. If we truly aspire to be a liberal and tolerant society, we'll make the effort of scrambling back up a ways, allowing smokers a few rooms to call their own.

BOOTLEGGERS AND BAPTISTS

One suspects that the conservatives of left and right don't much like the 'mass' and its badly informed preferences. Let us take care of you, they cry. Let tradition celebrated by wise elders, or planning implemented by wise experts, guide you, oh you sadly misled mass. And offstage the ancient lords and the cosy monopolists look on such conservative theorizing by the clerisy with delight, assured by it that their rents will be preserved.

— Deirdre McCloskey, *Bourgeois Equality*[1]

IN JUNE OF 2009, President Barack Obama signed the Family Smoking Prevention and Tobacco Control Act, the law giving the Food and Drug Administration authority over tobacco. In remarks at the White House Rose Garden, he acknowledged the guests in attendance who advocated for the law. Among them were representatives of the Campaign for Tobacco-Free Kids, the commissioner of the FDA, the director of the CDC, and several members of Congress. "Despite decades of lobbying and advertising by the tobacco industry," Obama said, "we've passed a law to help protect the next generation of Americans from growing up with a deadly habit that so many of our generation have lived with."[2]

Obama implied that the new law was a victory against Big Tobacco, but one of his most important allies went curiously unmentioned. That was Philip Morris, owner of Marlboro, the best-selling brand of cigarettes in the United States.[3] Representatives of Philip Morris and the Campaign for Tobacco-Free Kids had in fact conducted secret negotiations to hash out details of a bill that they could mutually support, a decision that alienated both Philip Morris's competitors and other anti-smoking groups.

Theirs was a reluctant coalition, as a 2004 article in *Roll Call* made clear. "We would never get in bed with these guys," said the executive director of the Campaign for Tobacco-Free Kids. "Philip Morris is the opponent." An executive at Philip Morris was equally insistent on denying ties to anti-smoking forces. "It's far from an alliance," he said. "We have a commonality of interests in seeing the same piece of legislation enacted." Despite their differences, the two sides ever so cautiously came together.[4] Tobacco executives didn't mind that anti-smoking activists received all the praise. "The name of the game was getting the bill, not getting credit," one explained.[5] This back-room dealing between avowed enemies may appear surprising, but it represents a new political strategy that benefits both anti-smoking groups and cigarette companies.

The typical model of tobacco regulation pits tobacco merchants on one side and public health activists and government officials squarely on the other. The former are assumed to pursue private self-interests while the latter are perceived as serving the public good. It's true that for much of history, from King James's lively *Counterblaste* to the Surgeon General's dry scientific reports, the two sides have often operated in opposition. The political landscape has changed, however, and today this model is simplistic, out of date, and a little bit naive.

Economists have long recognized that laws allegedly enacted for the public good often end up benefiting the very industries they are intended to regulate. They use the term "regulatory capture" to describe a situation in which regulators become unduly influenced by the regulated. As Adam Smith put it in *The Wealth of Nations*, "To widen the market and narrow the competition, is always in the interest of the dealers." Proposals that originate from industry must be examined "with the most suspicious attention," Smith warned, because they have "an interest to deceive and even to oppress the publick, and who accordingly have, upon many occasions, both deceived and oppressed it."[6]

This self-interested lobbying can lead to strange and unexpected alliances. Economist Bruce Yandle, a former director at the Federal Trade Commission, coined the memorable phrase "Bootleggers and Baptists" to describe these arrangements, citing the example of blue laws that forbid selling alcohol on Sundays.[7] Baptists support the laws because they favor temperance. Bootleggers support them because they drive Sunday drinkers to the black market. Though the Bootleggers and Baptists want nothing to do with each other, their separate incentives lead each of them to favor the restriction. The Baptists provide the public moral face of the argument while the Bootleggers quietly lobby politicians behind the scenes.

Applied more broadly, "the term 'Bootlegger' no longer implies illegal action but rather applies to political action in pursuit of narrow economic gains," explains a recent book co-authored by Yandle detailing how the logic of the Bootleggers and Baptists story plays out in real-world legislation. "Moreover, the term 'Baptist' does not necessarily indicate a religious motivation but rather group action driven by an avowed higher purpose or desire to serve the public interest." From alcohol to energy policy, the theory illuminates why many seemingly contradictory alliances work together in regulatory politics.[8]

What, Yandle asks, do the regulated want from the regulators? "They want protection from competition, from technological change, and from losses that threaten profits and jobs. A carefully constructed regulation can accomplish all kinds of anticompetitive goals of this sort, while giving the citizenry the impression that the only goal is to serve the public interest."[9] He wrote that in 1983, but he may as well have been describing Philip Morris two decades later.

For much of the twentieth century, an oppositional model adequately described the challenge of regulating tobacco sales. In the late 1990s, that model began to falter. The "Bootleggers" (Big Tobacco) and "Baptists" (health activists and public officials) started working together to achieve their mutual aims. The Master Settlement Agreement of 1998 and the Tobacco Control Act of 2009 are typically portrayed as landmark victories against the tobacco companies. In reality, they are partial victories at best, and they were cannily negotiated to protect the financial interests of the largest cigarette brands. In the new climate of tobacco control, it's more important than ever to ask the question, "Who benefits?" The answer, often, is Big Tobacco.

SETTLING WITH THE STATES

In most industries, if the corporations controlling 98% of the market colluded to raise prices, they would be prosecuted for anti-trust violations. In most industries, settling lawsuits to the tune of hundreds of billions of dollars would be a devastating blow to the bottom line. And in most industries, the defendants in those lawsuits would not be rewarded with laws that protect them from competition. Tobacco is not most industries. The Master Settlement Agreement of 1998 between state attorneys general and the leading cigarette makers, initially portrayed as a victory against Big Tobacco, has led instead to continuing profits for the corporations and a cozy relationship with state governments that have become financially dependent on cigarette revenues.

From the 1960s onward, tobacco companies managed to ward off liability lawsuits from grievously ill smokers by denying that any individual smoker's illness could be conclusively linked to tobacco use, arguing that risks were knowingly assumed by smokers, and throwing so much money into litigation that potential plaintiffs would be scared off by the costs of pursuing a case.[10] These tactics were remarkably successful: Though more than 800 cases were filed, only twenty-three were tried, only two held the companies even partially liable, and none resulted in the payment of damages.[11] In the late 1990s, however, the tobacco companies began facing a different kind of lawsuit that wasn't premised on harms to individual smokers. State governments themselves began seeking compensation for the tobacco-related health care costs of the entire smoking population, which were born by the states via Medicaid. This novel approach allowed state attorneys to avoid the murky business of trying to prove the cause of illness for any individual smoker. They could rely instead on statistical epidemiology at the population level, where the harms of smoking are impossible to deny.

Still, this was a new development in liability law and there were reasons to doubt its prospects for success. One question was whether states had standing to sue tobacco companies for decisions made by consumers. The Iowa state supreme court dismissed a lawsuit on the grounds that the state did not, and no state lawsuit had proceeded to a jury verdict by the time of the eventual settlement.[12] Another question was whether cigarette smokers did, in fact, have a negative impact on state treasuries. It's obviously true that there are medical costs associated with smoking, but smokers also cough up excise taxes every time they buy a pack. They also tend to die earlier than nonsmokers, which in the long-run reduces state government expenditures on pensions and health care. That's a grim calculation, and it's a persuasive reason not to take up cigarettes, but it undermined the core justification for the state lawsuits. Economist Kip Viscusi measured health expenditures associated with tobacco use against revenues from tobacco taxes and various cost reductions associated with lower life expectancy and concluded that smokers were paying their way in all fifty states, usually by a considerable margin.[13]

Despite these weaknesses, the tobacco companies had reasons to be wary. If they lost, the sums they would have owed were potentially astronomical. The states also had the power to amend their own laws in ways that would guarantee victory, a strategy they employed in Florida, Maryland, and Vermont.[14] And so in 1997, for the first time ever, Big Tobacco blinked. The companies approached the states with a proposal for a settlement of nearly $370 billion, which would have been the largest liability payout in the history of the United States.[15]

There was much more to this "Proposed Resolution" than a typical settlement. It came loaded with suggestions for legislation that would have drastically altered the regulation and marketing of tobacco. It proposed giving the Food and Drug Administration authority over cigarettes, requiring new warning labels on cigarette packages, establishing new initiatives to reduce youth smoking, imposing financial penalties if youth smoking reduction goals were not achieved, restricting cigarette advertising, and providing funding for a $500 million anti-smoking campaign. On top of the money paid to state governments, the cigarette companies would have also paid substantial legal fees to private law firms the states employed.[16]

Big Tobacco obviously expected something in return for these concessions. The primary benefit would have been immunity against future lawsuits. The resolution would have ended all lawsuits undertaken by state attorneys general, and the accompanying legislation would have shielded the tobacco companies from future civil lawsuits seeking damages for addiction or dependence, class actions, and lawsuits seeking punitive damages. The gamble was essentially that a huge settlement with the states that protected against future liability was preferable to the uncertainty of lawsuits in which juries might award enormous punitive damages.[17]

Whether this would have been a good deal for the tobacco companies will never be known: The Proposed Resolution fell apart for a variety of reasons, including lack of support at the federal level, public outcry against the protections from liability, and doubts within the public health community about negotiating with tobacco companies.[18] The proposal did, however, lay the groundwork for what would eventually become the Master Settlement Agreement (MSA) between the four largest tobacco companies and the state attorneys general. The companies initially settled lawsuits with Mississippi, Florida, Texas, and Minnesota for a combined payout of nearly $37 billion. In 1998, they settled with the remaining states for an additional $206 billion, bringing the total settlement to $243 billion. This ended litigation with the states, though it did nothing to protect the companies from individual and class action lawsuits. The MSA was also powerless to enact the earlier proposal that would have granted the FDA authority over cigarettes, but it did include provisions restricting advertising to youth and requiring the companies to dismantle industry-friendly research groups.[19]

The tobacco companies got less out of the MSA than they would have received from the Proposed Resolution, but it would nonetheless be a mistake to view the MSA as a pure victory against Big Tobacco. The settlement was the product of highly political backroom dealing unsupervised by judges, juries, legislators, or regulatory bodies. The payout was a financial bonanza for state governments and well-connected private attorneys and was structured in ways that converted the tobacco companies into a legally protected cartel. Smokers themselves did not receive a dime. In fact, they continue to pay for the settlement in perpetuity via higher cigarette prices. "The principal victims of the MSA were smokers," concluded American political scholar Martha Derthick. "They had few ways of protesting, being without representation in the process by which the MSA was constructed, and as disproportionately the poorest and least-educated part of the populace, they were not well-placed socially to mount a protest."[20]

As Viscusi notes in his book on the topic, in a typical settlement the tobacco companies would have paid the states a predetermined amount, either as a lump sum or over a period of time. Instead, the MSA allowed the amount to be determined by future cigarette sales; if sales declined, payments from the companies would decline as well. To fund the settlement, the companies were also permitted to collude on raising the price of cigarettes. The plan operated, in effect, as a hidden tax on smoking. Rather than pay the penalty for their misbehavior, the companies were allowed to pass the cost onto consumers.[21]

The obvious weakness in this arrangement is that it left Big Tobacco vulnerable to competition from new entrants to the market. New producers were not party to the MSA, so they could charge lower prices. The signatories had an interest in preventing that from happening, so the MSA included provisions to reduce the big tobacco companies' liability if they lost market share to non-participating competitors. As a result, all fifty states passed laws requiring cigarette companies that were not part of the MSA to either join the agreement or pay penalties that would be held in escrow for twenty-five years. Companies that may not have even existed at the time of the settlement were coerced into accepting its terms in order to protect the profits of Big Tobacco and the state governments' revenue stream.[22]

Who did benefit from the Master Settlement Agreement? It was obviously a windfall for the states. At the time of the settlement, it was assumed that much of the revenue would go toward covering health care expenditures and funding anti-smoking programs, but the money came without strings attached. In North Carolina, significant MSA revenues were actually devoted to supporting tobacco growers.[23] A national, ten-year retrospective concluded that a very small portion of the spending has gone toward smoking prevention. In fifteen states, no MSA funds were being spent on tobacco control at all. Most payments either went into general budgets or were sold as securities to private investors. Journalists have uncovered a variety of MSA expenditures completely unrelated to tobacco, such as spending on golf carts in New York, fiber optic lines in Virginia, flood control in North Dakota, and youth boot camps in Alabama.[24] These may or may not be worthwhile projects, but Big Tobacco can rest easy knowing that very little of their settlement cash is going toward smoking prevention.

Another beneficiary: the private law firms that assisted the states in litigation. The states' reliance on outside counsel in these lawsuits was unusual. Details of their fees are shrouded in secrecy, but well-connected attorneys — many of them campaign donors to their states' attorneys general — collected billions of dollars. Firms were awarded $3.4 billion in Florida, $3.3 billion in Texas, and $1.4 billion in Mississippi. Some firms claimed payments from multiple states.[25] Freedom of Information Act requests filed by the Chamber of Commerce revealed that attorneys' fees in twenty-one states totaled $11 billion.[26] These payouts were determined with little public scrutiny or demand for rigorous record-keeping. The money "vanished into the lawyers' pockets in a way studiously engineered to bypass public accountability," writes legal scholar Walter Olson, "a bold and piratical hijacking of public assets."[27]

How much the tobacco companies gained from the Master Settlement Agreement is a matter of debate. Lost avenues for advertising were offset by more aggressive marketing with retailers,[28] and the anti-competitive effects of the MSA enabled the companies to double the wholesale price of cigarettes by 2001.[29] The money they paid to states went toward everything but tobacco control, and the arrangement made states dependent on tobacco revenues. An executive at R. J. Reynolds boasted, "There's no doubt that the largest financial stakeholder in our industry is our state governments." This led to states enacting measures that protected tobacco companies from the costs of defending against class-action and individual lawsuits.[30]

In the end, states added billions to their general budgets. Private attorneys took billions to the bank. The tobacco companies paid billions to both, but in return they raised their prices, colluded against potential competitors, and avoided litigation. The most obvious financial loser from the settlement is the typical smoker, who pays higher prices and receives virtually nothing in return. Matt Myers of the Campaign for Tobacco Free-Kids, who helped negotiate the original proposed settlement, later reflected that the "tobacco companies counted on the greed and shortsightedness of politicians when they handed them billions of unexpected dollars, and they were right."[31]

Although the Master Settlement Agreement wasn't painless for the cigarette companies and they surely long for the *laissez-faire* heyday of the decades before, those days are over. The lesson they learned from the MSA is that rather than fighting the government, Big Tobacco can profitably work with it to game the system. It's a strategy Philip Morris would return to a few years later when lobbying for regulation by the Food and Drug Administration.

WELCOMING REGULATION

The FDA was granted authority over cigarettes by the Tobacco Control Act of 2009, which was backed by a coalition that included public health activists and tobacco giant Philip Morris.[32] Anti-smoking groups' reasons for supporting regulation are clear enough. The legislation subjected cigarettes to unprecedented scrutiny by the FDA, banned most tobacco flavors, forbade healthy-sounding words such as "light" in cigarette advertising, empowered the agency to remove products from the market, and opened the door to mandating reduced nicotine content.[33] But what was Philip Morris' motivation? Why did the nation's largest tobacco company support the law?

Reactions from other tobacco companies provide a clue. They derisively referred to the Tobacco Control Act as the "Marlboro Monopoly Act."[34] At the time of its passage, Philip Morris's Marlboro brand accounted for roughly 40% of cigarette sales in the United States. By supporting the bill, Philip Morris simultaneously burnished its public image,[35] eased fears that Congress might take more drastic steps to regulate the industry, and secured its hold on the market by making it more difficult for other brands to compete. The flavor ban also favored Philip Morris by exempting menthol, which the company uses in some of its brands, while forbidding flavors used by competitors R. J. Reynolds and Brown and Williamson.[36]

The most anti-competitive measure in the law requires the FDA to review new tobacco products before they are introduced for sale. Cigarettes that were already on the market as of February 15, 2007, were grandfathered in. Those introduced between then and March 22, 2011, have been allowed to stay on the market provisionally, although the FDA retains authority to order their removal. Crucially, no new products may be introduced after the latter date without first getting explicit approval from the FDA. As a result, the Tobacco Control Act essentially froze the market for cigarettes, protecting Marlboro's market share.

The Tobacco Control Act created two paths to approval for tobacco products. One is for completely new products, which requires a highly detailed review by the FDA. At this time, very few companies have attempted it. The other pathway is for products that are "substantially equivalent" to those already on the market in 2007. Products are considered substantially equivalent if they have the same "materials, ingredients, design, composition, heating source, and other features." The law also allows a finding of substantial equivalence when a product differs in its characteristics but raises no new questions of health. In other words, the FDA is tasked with ensuring that any changes in cigarette design would not encourage more people to take up smoking, discourage smokers from quitting, or raise new health concerns.

The law directs companies to submit applications for substantially equivalent products ninety days before they plan to take them to market, implying that the FDA's review would be completed quickly. The intent of the law is clear: to allow new cigarettes to get speedy approval if they don't make any significant innovations or raise new questions of health. That may seem reasonable, but in practice the FDA has often dragged out the process long beyond that deadline. A review by the Associated Press in 2013 found that since the law took effect, the agency had received approximately 3,500 substantial equivalence applications. It had more than one hundred employees working on reviewing them. And nearly four years later, the number of rulings it had issued was zero.[37]

It wasn't until June of 2013 that the FDA finally approved the first new cigarettes submitted under the substantial equivalence pathway. These were from Lorillard and were versions of their Newport brand, lightly modified to use fire-safe paper and omit menthol. That these changes raised no new questions of health was obvious.[38] Approving these cigarettes may have also helped the FDA avoid a legal battle with the tobacco company, which had publicly petitioned the agency to finally begin ruling on its backlog of applications.

Another landmark came in February of 2014 when the FDA exercised its power to order removal of cigarettes from the

American market for the first time. "It's a big deal," Matthew Myers of the Campaign for Tobacco-Free Kids told *The New York Times*. Mitch Zeller, director of the FDA's Center for Tobacco Products, called the order "historic" and said it "shows the role and power of regulation."[39] Countless news articles reported on the supposedly significant ruling. Which cigarette did the FDA order off store shelves? Was it a best-selling brand from Philip Morris? A cigarette targeting impressionable youth? A brand with some exceptionally carcinogenic additive? None of the above. It was Sutra, an obscure brand of Indian hand-rolled cigarettes known as bidis, that had already been off the American market for years. An attorney for the company told inquiring journalists that they had stopped exporting them to the United States in 2010.[40] That anti-smoking groups and the FDA portrayed this trifling victory as a "big deal" is indicative of just how little FDA regulation had actually affected popular brands of cigarettes.

After ten years of FDA regulation, it's worth asking whether the agency's lengthy review process is serving any useful purpose. It has managed to begin delivering decisions, approving 255 substantial equivalence applications in its most recent fiscal year. (It also rejected 87 applications and 227 were withdrawn by the applicants.)[41] The FDA contends that minor differences in the composition or design of cigarettes can make them significantly more dangerous or more addictive. But if this is true, so is the reverse: Minor differences could also make cigarettes significantly less dangerous or less addictive. As Michael Siegel notes, this represents a reversal from past practice when it was the cigarette companies who made that misleading claim:

My opinion is that most, if not all of the substantial

equivalence applications involve minor changes that have no substantial bearing on altering the public health significance or impact of the products. [...] Cigarettes are, by their nature, so hazardous that these changes do not merit such protracted scrutiny. But it is important to recognize that the FDA is creating harm not merely by wasting time and resources, but by framing the issue of cigarette toxicity in the opposite way that we in tobacco control have been framing it for decades.[42]

Similar doubts were raised during debate over the Tobacco Control Act by none other than the agency's then commissioner, Andrew C. von Eschenbach. "Associating the Agency with the approval of these inherently dangerous products would undermine the Agency's mission," he wrote in a 2007 statement to Congress.[43] He also presciently warned that the deadlines imposed by the law would not give the FDA enough time to create science-based rules and would "unduly and unfairly raise the public's expectations about what the Agency could accomplish." The agency's unimpressive track record has proven him correct. The contrast between the first cigarettes the agency approved and the first it ordered off the market — the former from a big, politically influential tobacco company, the latter from a foreign producer with very little presence in the United States — suggests that the agency's decisions were driven as much by political expediency as by legitimate scientific criteria.

Micah Berman, professor of public health and law at Ohio State University and a former adviser to the FDA, notes in a working paper that "the promise that the TCA's enactment would be a transformative moment for public health has not been fulfilled." Anti-smoking groups expected FDA regulation to enable aggressive restrictions on the tobacco industry; the

industry expected it to insulate big companies from competition. "Under the Obama administration," writes Berman, "the
tobacco industry's view of how the law would function was far
closer to the reality."[44]

Additional evidence for this view comes from the experience of David Sley, one of the few entrepreneurs to attempt
launching a new cigarette company in the time since the agency
began regulating the market. Sley created a brand under the
name Hestia Tobacco. Although the FDA's process for
reviewing cigarettes is opaque, documents provided by Sley
demonstrate how its bureaucracy keeps new cigarettes off the
market without examining questions of health. Merely getting
approval for the Hestia brand name required eight inquiries
with three different FDA officials over the course of an entire
year.

Sley submitted his substantial equivalence application for
Hestia in June of 2012. As required by the FDA, his application
compared Hestia to a predicate product already on the market,
Natural American Spirits. The two cigarettes are, by any
reasonable interpretation of the words, substantially equivalent. Four months after submitting his application, the FDA
responded with a letter requesting eight more categories of
information, including "a comparison of your new tobacco
product and predicate tobacco product with respect to heating
source" — in other words, how are the cigarettes lit? (Answer:
With fire.) Sley responded as best as he was able and
beseeched regulators to rule on his product. "We want a
license to fail," he wrote. "The freedom to see if consumers
want this product. We're just asking for the ability to market
our product, and see if it sells. Currently, we remain unable to
do so." Under such a burdensome regime, it's clear that big
tobacco companies have the upper hand against upstart

competitors. By attempting to launch his own company, Sley discovered that competing with Big Tobacco in the twenty-first century is as difficult as it was in the days of Buck Duke's mighty tobacco trust. Today it's not the cutthroat tactics of the trust that prevent competition; it's regulation by the Food and Drug Administration.

CIGARS IN THE CROSSFIRE

Imagine what it would be like if the FDA's restrictions on cigarettes were applied to a widely consumed product such as beer. There would have been only two new beers allowed on the market for the first several years of regulation. Beers introduced since 2007 could be ordered off the market at any time. Any new beers would have to prove themselves substantially equivalent to beers that were being sold a decade ago. There would be no new hop varieties, no new styles, certainly none of the odd, innovative recipes that craft brewers dream up. The situation might be good for big, established breweries seeking to preserve market share for the industrial lagers they've sold for decades, but it would be terrible for beer lovers and small producers.

Or imagine an even more extreme proposal: Imagine that the government required that nearly all the alcohol be removed from beer, taking the content down to almost zero. Would the drinks remaining on the market in this scenario meaningfully qualify as beer? Any proposal to regulate the beverage this way would elicit an outcry from consumers and a flood of news stories sympathetic to brewers. Journalists drink a lot of beer, after all, and craft beer possesses cultural cachet. Tobacco does not. That's likely one reason why FDA regulation of traditional ways of smoking has received so little attention. But as implausible as the scenarios outlined above may seem, they may soon be the reality for pipes and cigars.

When the FDA gained authority over tobacco in 2009, its regulations applied only to cigarettes, smokeless tobacco, and roll-your-own tobacco. In 2016, however, the agency expanded its purview to include all forms of tobacco and nicotine vapor products, applying the restrictions of the Tobacco Control Act to cigars, pipes, and e-cigarettes (the last of which are the topic of the next chapter).[45] Although they were not the initial target of legislation, pipes and cigars are caught in the crossfire of the Bootleggers and Baptists politics of tobacco regulation. Big Tobacco benefits by raising the costs faced by these potential competitors, and the moral case for regulation is provided by anti-smoking groups, many of them funded in part by cigarette makers' own MSA payments. The new restrictions will make these dynamic markets much less competitive, resulting in reduced choice and variety for consumers.

FDA regulations will force small producers of premium cigars to shoulder the same regulatory burdens as giant companies like Philip Morris. If pre-market review is inconvenient for the relatively commodified cigarette market, it will be devastating for premium cigars. The FDA estimates that there are more than 7,500 separate cigar products in the United States, and cigar makers release hundreds of new cigars in various shapes, sizes, and blends of tobacco every year.[46] But for new cigars to get through the FDA's review process, they would have to be explicitly modeled after cigars already on the market in 2007. The agency's own analysis predicts that the initial costs of compliance for cigars, pipe tobacco, and pipes will exceed $20 million. The average cost of submitting a full substantial equivalence application is expected to exceed $22,000 and require 220 hours of preparation, a burden that would apply to a quarter of all new cigar applications.[47]

At the FDA's current pace of approving cigarettes, only a fraction of new cigars would make it through the process and all the cigars that have been released since 2007 would face removal from the market. Given the high costs of completing an application, the slow pace of review, and the uncertain odds of success, many cigar brands will not bother attempting to introduce new offerings. The FDA predicts that roughly 5% of the newly deemed combustible tobacco products will simply exit the market, including many small batch items.[48] The agency dismisses this loss of variety as being of little importance to the consumer:

> We lack a baseline estimate of consumer valuation of tobacco product variety, making it impossible to estimate how consumers who continue to use tobacco products would value the potential loss of variety due to product exit under this final rule. Today we see very large numbers of products embodying minor variations. Even if considerable product consolidation were to occur, close substitutes would exist for discontinued products, which would limit the size of any ongoing impact on consumers who switch to a substitute product. However, there will be some one-time costs for searching for a suitable substitute when products exit the market. We do not quantify these search costs here.[49]

A return to the beer analogy suggests that this stagnation would impose a real cost on cigar smokers. The market for cigarettes is comparable to the market for broadly appealing lagers like Budweiser or Coors. It is dominated by a few big brands that are fairly interchangeable, distinguished by their marketing and brand identities. If the FDA regulated beer the same way it regulates cigarettes, these are the kind of beers the agency would favor. Cigars, in contrast, are more like the craft beer segment of the market. There are thousands of options, each defined by the origin of its ingredients, its particular blend of tobaccos, the shape of the cigar, the skill of the rollers, and its period of ageing. The FDA's micro-managed regulatory model is ill-suited to this sort of artisanal process, and regulators will unavoidably stifle the cigar market by trying to apply it.

Perhaps that would be a worthwhile trade-off if the FDA is actually effective at sorting healthier products from those that are more dangerous. It's debatable whether it successfully does this for cigarettes, which are among the most extensively studied consumer products in history. How could it possibly do so for cigars? If a cigar producer decides to switch from a Dominican to a Nicaraguan wrapper, or from a corona size to a robusto, what kind of evidence could conceivably satisfy the FDA's mandate to consider how that change would affect initiation, cessation, and health, not just for an individual smoker, but for the entire population of the United States? Cigar manufacturing is replete with minor decisions about leaf source, size, shape, and method of production. It would be impossible to measure the impact of these choices at a population level, forcing the FDA to feign an impossible degree of foresight.

Even more worrying is the possibility that the FDA will mandate the removal of nicotine in all forms of combustible tobacco.[50] This would, in essence, make it illegal to sell the combustible tobacco products favored by cigarette, cigar, and pipe smokers throughout the United States. This controversial idea was championed by the most recent commissioner of the FDA, Scott Gottlieb. He announced his intentions in July of 2017 when he envisioned "a world where cigarettes would no longer create or sustain addiction, and where adults who still need or want nicotine could get it from alternative and less harmful sources."[51]

Technically, the FDA is forbidden by law from requiring the complete elimination of nicotine in tobacco, but it could mandate that nicotine be reduced to near zero. The idea is that by doing so new smokers would never get addicted and current smokers would be forced to quit or turn elsewhere for their fix. In the ideal scenario, cigarette smokers would switch to safer e-cigarettes or similar devices. Realistically, many of them will choose to stick with actual tobacco, sourcing it on the black market or buying it in other legal forms such as roll-your-own, pipe tobacco, and both small and premium cigars. Therein lies the threat for people who enjoy smoking any of those products. Cigarette smokers who switch to these would partially offset the gains of regulation, inviting further intervention. A nicotine rule that begins by targeting only cigarettes would likely end up affecting all forms of combustible tobacco.

This is no idle speculation. Anti-smoking organizations are actively and explicitly pressuring the FDA to mandate low nicotine yields across the board. According to comments signed by a bevy of anti-smoking groups, "There is no rational basis for reducing nicotine levels in cigarettes, while leaving cigars highly addictive... Exempting cigars from a reduced nicotine standard is likely to lead current cigarette smokers to switch to cigars or use both cigarettes and cigars to satisfy their need for nicotine."[52] The FDA's own analysis similarly concludes that extending its authority to all forms of tobacco would be necessary "to rectify an institutional failure in which tobacco products that are close substitutes are not regulated by the FDA in a like manner."[53]

Whether Congress intended for the commissioner of the

FDA to wield such power is debatable. The Tobacco Control Act prohibits the agency from banning entire classes of tobacco products or requiring the complete removal of nicotine. Mandating near-zero nicotine yields would accomplish essentially the same thing, perhaps complying with the letter of the law but clearly ignoring its spirit. "By continuing to advance this measure," Carrie Wade and Clive Bates argue in a policy study for the R Street Institute, "the FDA takes Congress literally but not seriously, and the agency would do well to recognize that Congress expects to authorize rulemaking of this significance."[54] It would be an anti-democratic power grab for a regulatory agency to take this action unilaterally, substantially affecting millions of stakeholders without accountability.

If the FDA essentially prohibits nicotine in cigars and other tobacco products, the act of smoking them will be fundamentally changed — a real cost to the consumers who enjoy them. Anti-smoking groups implausibly deny this, contending that the rule wouldn't result in any loss of utility for cigar smokers because they would still be allowed to obtain nicotine from patches, gums, or e-cigarettes. "To the extent that smokers derive pleasure from smoking apart from satisfying their need for nicotine, they will continue to be able to purchase cigarettes and other combusted products," they argue in their comments to the FDA. "Having access to both nicotine and combusted tobacco products, it is questionable whether smokers will experience any loss of consumer surplus, even assuming that such surplus is generated by smoking."[55]

In other words, their argument is that smoking a nicotine-free cigar with a dose of nicotine on the side is just as good as having the real thing. If it sounds ridiculous when it's phrased that way, that's because it is. It's nonsense and would be seen as such in any other context. No one would reasonably suggest that a non-alcoholic beer accompanied by a shot of vodka is an adequate substitute for an IPA, or that a cup of decaf and a caffeine pill is just as satisfying as an espresso. Sometimes a cigar is just a cigar — but not when it's been chemically stripped of its essential attributes.

Although research rarely investigates the pleasurable effects of smoking, experimental comparison of smokers' responses to regular cigarettes and to a combination of denicotinized cigarettes and nicotine patches provides further reason for skepticism: In a blind study, smokers rated the normal cigarettes as consistently more pleasant and enjoyable.[56] Yet advocates of denicotinizing tobacco act as if complex sensory experiences can be sliced and diced into separate components with no loss to the whole. It's true that nicotine is part of the experience of smoking — sometimes even the most important part — but smokers aren't robots. If they were motivated by nothing more than getting a jolt of nicotine to their systems, pharmaceutical companies would have solved the problem of smoking long ago.

Nonetheless, the argument might persuade the FDA. The agency has struggled for years over whether to treat premium cigars differently from other tobacco products, likely because any threat to them will meet with organized political resistance. One of the FDA's early proposals attempted to draw a line between premium cigars and the smaller cigars and cigarillos that are more worrisome with regard to youth initiation, exempting the former from pre-market review.[57] Cigar makers have also been pushing their own bill in Congress to exempt premium cigars, although it will be a struggle to get it passed.[58]

It's possible that premium cigars will be initially exempted from new nicotine requirements, but that special treatment would survive at the whim of future FDA commissioners. They will likely be inclined to revoke it for the sake of consistency or in response to cigarette smokers who turn to cigars as the last legal source of tobacco containing nicotine. The logic of the Bootleggers and Baptists political dynamic predicts that anti-smoking groups and the Big Tobacco companies would unite in favor of extending the regulation to cigars, the former to promote better health and the latter to restrict competition. Sooner or later, the proposal to cap nicotine content would end up affecting all traditional tobacco products.

Despite its nominally libertarian ethos, the United States is poised to become one of the most restrictive countries in the world when it comes to smoking. This has implications not just for those who enjoy traditional tobacco, but also for the millions of cigarette smokers who are switching to much safer e-cigarettes. When Philip Morris began lobbying for FDA regulation in the early 2000s, it was impossible to predict the degree to which vaping would revolutionize the market. Today the agency is stifling innovation and undermining the potential of these products to reduce the harms of smoking. Threats of regulation and the high costs of compliance are once again tilting the playing field in favor of Big Tobacco, jeopardizing the future of this unforeseen competitor to the cigarette.

NON-BURNING ISSUES

When a country protects itself from change too enthusiastically, it robs itself of the new information, ideas, and behaviors that might make for a better country. When most people's natural fear of the new is supported by law, the law justifies the fear, thus institutionalizing prejudice against anything new and different.
— Peter McWilliams, *Ain't Nobody's Business if You Do*[1]

"THERE'S AN EPIDEMIC SPREADING," warns a dramatic video from the Food and Drug Administration.[2] "Scientists say it can change your brain," the voice-over continues as the camera zooms into a teenager's cranium to reveal grotesque wormlike creatures tunneling into gray matter. The camera pans to other high school students' veins visibly swelling with contagion as additional dangers are listed. What is this disgusting new threat? "It's not a parasite, not a virus, not an infection. It's vaping."[3]

It's a strange way to talk about a technology that FDA leaders say they believe will play a vital role in reducing the harms associated with smoking. Teenagers are the intended audience of the video, but its portrayal of vaping is so repulsive that the agency attempted to minimize the number of adults who watch it. "Adults should not be seeing these ads," said Mitch Zeller, director of the FDA's Center for Tobacco Products, introducing the campaign at a forum hosted by New York University.[4] That's because the agency is wary of discouraging adult smokers from switching to e-cigarettes, which most scientists agree carry substantially lower risks than combustible tobacco. But ads like this one contribute to a hostile political climate that has put e-cigarettes under attack at all levels of government.

This wave of legislation is the predictably panicked response to disruptive technology. E-cigarettes grew rapidly in popularity and developed without the input of pharmaceutical companies or health officials. They deliver nicotine in ways that resemble a real cigarette but without the high dose of carcinogenic chemicals that are produced by burning tobacco leaves. A growing body of evidence suggests that they will benefit public health by competing against cigarettes, helping people to quit smoking, to smoke less often, or to never take up smoking in the first place. Government agencies have failed to communicate these benefits, however, doing more to stoke fears about vaping than to convince smokers to switch. At the same time, ideologically motivated anti-smoking groups have demonized vapor products in the media, causing the public to remain grossly uninformed about how they differ from conventional cigarettes.

As with past debates about secondhand smoke and smoking bans, the controversy over e-cigarettes cannot be reduced to simple disagreement about empirical evidence. The hostility to vaping reflects long-standing prejudice against the consumption of nicotine for pleasure. Previous chapters documented the ways in which the anti-smoking movement gradually morphed into a campaign to stigmatize both the act of smoking and smokers themselves, banishing them from public spaces and denying their agency as consenting adults. These attitudes have carried over to vaping. Its sudden popularity challenges the biases of anti-smoking activists not because it is harmful, but because it is safer: The practice threatens to re-normalize the sin of enjoying nicotine without the wages of premature death.

This moralistic aspect of the anti-vaping campaign has enabled restrictions on public e-cigarette use to proceed without evidence of actual harm to bystanders, merely on the basis that they sort of resemble the real thing. "It's similar to smoking," one Washington, DC, city council member explained when the District expanded its existing smoking ban to cover e-cigarettes. "We don't know what the ill effects of this are, and it's still a bother to some people."[5]

"Similar to smoking" and "a bother." Efforts to include vaping under anti-smoking statutes have arisen as if in proof of Marx's dictum that history repeats itself first as tragedy, then as farce. In the debates over bans on actual smoking, advocates at least attempted to offer evidence of harm, even if their claims were often exaggerated. In the moral panic over e-cigarettes, they don't trouble with the effort.

The justification for banning vaping offered by health offi-cials in my own city is representative: Vaping indoors, reads the report from the Board of Health for Multnomah County, "threatens to undermine compliance with strong smoking regulations and reverse the progress that has been made in establishing a social norm that smoking is not permitted in public places or places of employment."[6] Health officials in Seattle offered a similar reasoning, noting that "by returning smoking to the public eye, public e-cigarette use threatens to undermine the social norming impact [of smoking bans]."[7] Or as the health minister of France put it, "This is no ordinary product because it encourages mimicking and could promote taking up smoking."[8]

Never mind that vaping is not smoking or whether it is really so confusing that the former may be permitted in some places where the latter is not. What's notable is how easily the justification shifted from preventing harm to bystanders to policing behavior that merely looks like smoking. The anti-smoking movement's empirically unmoored response to the public use of e-cigarettes is one of the clearest expressions yet of its hostility to individual liberty and its commitment to stig-matizing nicotine use in any form.

Regrettably, the inclusion of vaping under smoking bans is only one among many threats to the future of e-cigarettes. Hard-liners in the anti-smoking movement demand abstinence not just from smoking but from any use of nicotine that brings enjoyment to the user. Instead of congratulating smokers when they began turning to vaping, they have worked to forbid the sale of e-cigarettes, tax them, raise the legal age of purchase, ban flavors, and frighten smokers away from ever giving them a try.

The most vocal and politically effective voices in tobacco control have always been the most dogmatic, but thankfully there is a more moderate and pragmatic wing of health researchers who are cautiously embracing less harmful competitors to the cigarette. If expecting complete abstinence from nicotine is as unrealistic as it is for other pleasures — and we have centuries of reasons to believe that it is — then allowing these safer alternatives to compete is more humane than chasing utopian dreams of a nicotine-free future. This chapter looks at what we currently know about the risks and benefits of tobacco harm reduction and details the myriad ways that ideologically motivated activists have attempted to stifle promising technologies and restrict the free choices of consenting adults, actively undermining innovations that offer life-saving benefits for smokers.

How the Swedes stopped smoking

Before getting into the science of e-cigarettes, it's worth gauging their potential for harm reduction by examining how safer ways of consuming nicotine have already brought about beneficial health outcomes in countries where residents have access to them. The best models we have for this are Sweden and Norway. Both are home to extensive use of a type of oral tobacco called snus (pronounced "snoose," like "loose" in English). In contrast to American oral tobaccos, snus doesn't trigger the intense salivation that requires users to constantly spit. It's cleaner and more discreet; one could spend hours with a person using snus and be none the wiser. But its advantages go beyond the aesthetic: Snus has helped Sweden and Norway achieve some of the world's lowest rates of smoking and smoking-related diseases. Since snus is not widely consumed anywhere else, these two countries offer a natural experiment in what happens when lethal cigarettes face competition from safer alternatives. Their experiences show decisively that tobacco harm reduction can save lives.

Snus originated in Sweden and has its roots in snuff. Much like the United States and many other countries, in the early twentieth century Swedes abandoned oral tobacco in favor of modern cigarettes. By the mid-1900s, oral tobacco had become a habit of the elderly; younger Swedes smoked. But unlike other countries, when the dangers of cigarettes were publicized in the 1960s, Swedish men turned to snus instead. This transition stands out strikingly in surveys of how Swedes report initiating tobacco use. Swedish women of any living generation began almost exclusively with cigarettes. The same was true for Swedish men born in the 1940s. Beginning in the 1960s, however, Swedish men shifted toward initiating via snus. This preference has increased over time; a majority of males born in the 1980s never took up daily tobacco use at all, and most of those who did chose snus, not cigarettes.[9]

Norwegian adoption of snus began later, but rates of smoking have been falling steadily there, too, as the preference for snus increases. The share of the Norwegian population using snus eclipsed that smoking cigarettes in 2017, with smoking rates falling from 21% of the population to 11% in just one decade. Over the same period, the rate of snus usage doubled.[10]

When anti-smoking groups speak of victory against smoking, they often define the target as reducing population-level use of tobacco to 5% or less. Achieving that would require significant reductions in the United States and the European Union, where cigarette smoking rates among adults sit at around 14% and 18%, respectively. But among younger cohorts in Sweden and Norway, the rate is already phenomenally low. Among Norwegians aged sixteen to twenty-four, only 5% of men and 1% of women report daily smoking.[11] In Sweden the rate among eighteen-year-olds has fallen to around 4%,[12] and the rates for all ages have fallen to less than 8% of men and 10% of women. This gives Sweden the lowest rates of daily smoking in the European Union by a substantial margin.[13]

The low rates of smoking among Swedish men translate to superior health outcomes. Aside from tiny Liechtenstein, they can boast the lowest rate of mortality due to lung cancer in the EU at just forty-two annual deaths per 100,000 men. Next place Finland isn't close, coming in at nearly 60/100,000. The rate for European men as a whole is 85/100,000, peaking at 139/100,000 in cigarette-loving Hungary.[14] For all causes of death attributable to tobacco use, Swedish men die at a much lower rate than the average European male.[15]

The observation that low rates of smoking lead to low rates of smoking-related mortality is hardly surprising. What some observers do find surprising is that these exceptional health outcomes have been achieved without abstinence from tobacco. Tobacco use in Sweden and Norway is still robust; it has simply shifted to forms that are much safer than cigarettes. The Scandinavian experience shows that significant gains in public health can be achieved by persuading people to give up smoking even if they don't give up tobacco or nicotine altogether.

The success of Sweden and Norway brings up a few obvious questions. One is whether, despite all the apparent good news, snus presents dangers of its own that offset the gains from reduced smoking. The short answer is no. "For Swedish snus, a convincing epidemiological evidence base shows no associations with lung cancer or respiratory diseases, and very weak, if any, association with cardiovascular diseases," write Karl Lund and Tord Vedoy of the Norwegian Institute of Public Health in a recent study. "Moreover, there is no evidence that use of Swedish snus is associated with any major health hazard that does not also arise from tobacco smoking."[16]

The methods of production used in making snus render it chemically distinct from older American-style chewing tobacco and other oral tobaccos, complicating comparisons between different countries and time periods. Over the course of the

1980s and 1990s, Swedish snus producers developed standards to minimize carcinogenic constituents created by microbial growth and fire-curing of tobacco. Contemporary snus is made with air-cured tobacco leaves and a steam heating process that results in much lower concentrations of nitrosamines and other potentially harmful substances.[17] A meta-analysis of thirty-seven studies from different geographic regions found significant elevated oral cancer risks for several types of oral tobacco, but not for snus.[18] Similarly, a review of eighty-nine American and Scandinavian studies found significant associations in studies of older American chewing tobaccos, but not for snus.[19] Another review was suggestive of associations with other rare cancers, but found no association between snus and oral cancer.[20]

Cardiac risks are a more plausible concern, raising the question of how long-term nicotine use divorced from other constituents of tobacco smoke affects coronary health. This is a matter of ongoing and controversial research, and because the potential effects are small, they are difficult to pin down with precision. There is limited evidence that snus elevates mortality risk among users who already suffer from cardiovascular disease, though it may not be a significant cause of the disease itself.[21] However, a 2018 meta-analysis found no increased risk of heart disease and stroke associated with Swedish snus.[22]

What is not controversial is that using snus is far safer than rolling tobacco leaves into a paper tube, lighting them on fire, and habitually inhaling the smoke deep into one's lungs. A panel of experts evaluating the evidence in 2004 came to a consensus that the overall mortality risk of snus is likely less than 10% that of cigarettes.[23] Research in the intervening years has served only to strengthen the conclusion that snus is far less likely to cause fatal diseases in its users.

A second question is whether snus has actually contributed to Sweden and Norway's abandonment of smoking or if, as some critics allege, it has merely kept potential quitters hooked on tobacco in a different guise. Perhaps, they argue, these countries' phenomenally low rates of smoking would be just as low or even lower in the absence of snus. Or worse, what if snus acts as a gateway to smoking, promotes dual-use of snus and cigarettes, and inhibits cessation? (These charges will be familiar to anyone who follows American debates over vaping.)

Evidence at the population level suggests that none of these fears are borne out by experience. Survey data from more than 60,000 Swedes found that the proportion of daily nicotine users who primarily smoke cigarettes declined substantially at the same time that the popularity of snus was rising. Fewer primary snus users become smokers than do Swedes who never or only occasionally use snus; the product appears to act as a substitute for smoking rather than a gateway. Researchers analyzing these results concluded that they "completely discount gateway as a credible hypothesis, at least for snus use in Sweden. If any gateway exists, it is dwarfed by other factors which are net protective."[24]

Snus also appears effective as an aid to quitting smoking, although this surprisingly has not often been studied in a clinical context. Survey data shows that snus is the most popular cessation aid among Swedish men, accounting for half of aided quit attempts. These potential quitters report the highest rate of success, nearly double that of those who try nicotine patches and gums.[25] Similar results have been reported for Norway.[26]

The Swedish report also rebuts the charge that snus leads to sustained dual-use:

Almost one-third of secondary snus users eventually quit all snus use and became entirely tobacco-free. This finding refutes the common assumption that uptake of snus use would entail lifelong perpetuation of nicotine dependence, based on the belief that snus use is as addictive as smoking. [...We] found that more than eight out of ten secondary snus users had quit daily smoking and that almost one-third of them had become completely free of daily tobacco use. Consequently, there are strong reasons to assume that 'dual use' is usually a transient rather than permanent state or an endpoint. It could then be seen as part of a multistep behavioral change where primary daily smokers use secondary uptake of snus as a stepping-stone towards changing/quitting their tobacco use.[27]

And so, a final question: If snus is so great, why aren't smokers in other countries using it to quit? The simplest answer is that their governments won't let them. The European Union banned the sale of many kinds of oral tobacco in 1992. This was a sticking point for Sweden's entry to the EU, which was contingent upon securing an exemption to the snus ban. This was enacted by treaty in 1995.[28] In the time since then, Sweden and Norway (the latter is not a member of the EU) have been the only countries whose residents have enjoyed sustained access to this safer alternative.

Snus became available in the United States fairly recently, though it remains a very niche part of the tobacco market. This is likely due in part to its association with chewing tobacco, since the differences between chew and snus are not obvious to the casual consumer. The FDA also forbids snus companies from marketing their product as a lower risk alternative to cigarettes, so potential consumers in America are denied the information they need to make an informed choice on the matter.[29] Note again the Bootleggers and Baptists logic of FDA tobacco regulation: Anti-smoking activists who publicly oppose allowing snus producers to advertise the relative safety of their products end up protecting American cigarette companies from competition.[30]

In the United States and other Western countries, it may turn out that snus will be less relevant to harm reduction efforts than newer technologies such as e-cigarettes. But the success of snus serves as a positive model regardless of whether the product itself catches on here. Advocates of harm reduction can take heart from the experiences of Sweden and Norway, both of which strongly suggest that competition from safer alternatives can drive down rates of smoking and reduce the toll of fatal diseases associated with combustible tobacco.

INNOVATING E-CIGARETTES FROM THE BOTTOM-UP

Whether it's snus in Scandinavia or e-cigarettes elsewhere, the logic in favor of tobacco harm reduction is simple: "People smoke for nicotine but they die from the tar," as tobacco researcher Michael Russell famously observed in 1976.[31] That's an oversimplification, but it expresses the truth that while nicotine plays an essential role in making smoking addictive, it's other components of tobacco smoke that are most deadly. If there were a satisfying way to deliver the former without the latter, then most of the harm that comes from smoking cigarettes could be avoided.

Alas, it turns out this is easier said than done. R. J. Reynolds attempted in 1988 to launch the world's first smokeless cigarette, a device that used a carbon rod to heat a combination of real tobacco and a capsule containing nicotine and tobacco extracts. Dubbed Premier, it was intended to bring the company back to the top of the American cigarette market. But

Premier was difficult to light and smoke, reacted malodorously with the sulfur in matches, and produced a distinctly unpleasant taste. One consumer described it as smelling "like burning tennis sneakers;" another likened it to opening "a grave on a warm day." It also didn't help that Reynolds was attempting to market a safer cigarette while publicly denying the dangers of smoking. Premier was a financial catastrophe, going down as one of the great flops in marketing history.[32]

The nicotine patches, gums, and inhalers marketed by pharmaceutical companies have fared better commercially, but they also fall short of being a substitute for cigarettes. Medical reviews find that using them increases the odds that a quit attempt will be successful, but most people who try them go right back to smoking. Over-the-counter availability of nicotine replacement therapies has had minimal effects on population-level cessation rates.[33] While there is truth to Russell's statement that "people smoke for nicotine," it's also true that they smoke for more complex aspects of the experience that aren't replicated by mechanical delivery of the chemical to the bloodstream. Tobacco and pharmaceutical companies have both attempted to create satisfying alternatives, but with the exception of snus, they have largely failed to create products capable of competing with the conventional cigarette.

The electronic cigarette has proven capable of competing, and it originated from an entirely different source. Credit for bringing the first e-cigarette to market goes to Beijing pharmacist Hon Lik. A smoker himself, Hon had witnessed his father succumb to lung cancer. This loss motivated him to invent the device that forms the conceptual basis for contemporary e-cigarettes. Hon's design consisted of a battery for power; a cartridge of liquid nicotine, propylene glycol, water, and flavorings; and an atomizer that converts the liquid into vapor. It hit the Chinese market in 2004 under the name Ruyan, meaning "smoke-like."[34]

Later e-cig designs took the form of what we now call a "cigalike," a self-contained device that resembles a real cigarette in size, shape, and appearance, often including an LED at the tip to mimic burning tobacco leaf. Notable brands include V2, Blu, and NJOY. Early e-cigarette brands launched or purchased by traditional tobacco companies often take this form, making them a ready fit for convenience stores and other typical cigarette retail locations.[35]

Some of the most important innovations in e-cigarette design went in a different direction, one that once again was driven by neither Big Tobacco nor Big Pharma. Increased battery power was pursued by vapers who hacked power sources from items like flashlights and laser pointers to incorporate them into e-cigarettes. "Modders" exchanged techniques in online forums, driving a transition away from devices that were constrained by the form-factor of a conventional cigarette. The diverse market for flavored e-liquids was also driven by a do-it-yourself ethos among vapers and small manufacturers. Eventually, nearly every component of e-cigarettes could be customized by the user.[36] "Vapers have been crucial to this process, as consumers, innovators, and standard setters," conclude Julian Morris and Amir Ullah Kahn in a paper for the Reason Foundation. "It is no exaggeration to describe this process as a revolution from the bottom-up: It was driven by consumers from the beginning."[37]

As popular as these customizable e-cigs are, one disadvantage is that they require consumers to spend time and money figuring out which combinations best suit their particular needs. That's fine for enthusiasts, but it's an obstacle for more casual adopters. In 2015, a Silicon Valley company addressed this shortcoming with a product called Juul. *Wired* hailed it as "the first great e-cig" and made comparisons to the iPhone for its sleek design, ease of use, and potential to revolutionize the market. Perhaps most importantly, the device offered a unique means of nicotine delivery, vaporizing nicotine salts that offer higher bioavailability than the vapor from typical e-cigs.[38] Juul better mimicked the dose and feel of conventional cigarettes and the company soon dominated the retail market for vaping. By October 2018 it could boast a corporate valuation of $15 billion, outperforming vapor brands owned by Big Tobacco.[39] Later that year, that success attracted investment from Philip Morris USA parent company Altria, which now has a 35% stake in the company.[40]

Outside of the United States, conventional tobacco companies are reviving a surprising technology: the heat-not-burn idea that tanked for R. J. Reynolds in the 1980s. The new generation of heat-not-burn is exemplified by IQOS, a product that Philip Morris International is counting on to replace cigarettes as they decline in popularity and social acceptability. The design of IQOS superficially resembles an e-cigarette but functions completely differently. It comes in two main parts, an electronic holder that generates heat and tiny cigarettes made of real tobacco. The tobacco in these "HeatSticks" is specially treated to generate a flavorful nicotine-laden vapor when heated by the device, which keeps the temperature below the point of combustion.[41] IQOS mimics the experience of smoking actual tobacco with fewer harmful constituents than are generated by burning it. As of now it's difficult to make confident predictions about its potential for harm reduction, but it does appear to be a credibly safer alternative to cigarettes for individual smokers. Philip Morris persuaded the FDA to allow its sale in the United States in early 2019.[42]

While all of these innovations were in development, the threat of FDA regulation loomed over the vapor industry. Early on, the FDA attempted to ban the importation of e-cigarettes entirely until a federal judge ruled in 2010 that it lacked authority to do so.[43] When the agency later announced that it would begin regulating them the same way it does cigarettes, there was fear that thousands of different products would be ordered off the market, potentially sending millions of vapers back to far more dangerous combustible tobacco.

Unlike conventional cigarettes, which can win approval from the FDA by proving themselves substantially equivalent to products that were already on the market in 2007, the vast majority of e-cigarette producers will have to meet a much vaguer standard, convincing regulators that approving their products will be "appropriate for the protection of the public health."[44] No one knows exactly what that will entail, but we do know that it will be outrageously expensive. The FDA's own economic impact analysis estimated that the cost of application would average $466,563 for e-cigarette hardware and $131,643 for e-liquids; for hardware, that works out to more than $80,000 per device.[45] The cost for the pathway used for conventional tobacco, in contrast, was estimated at just $22,700.[46] In other words, the regulatory costs associated with introducing a vapor device will be many times that of introducing a cigarette, despite the desirability of the former competing with the latter.

Given these hurdles, one may wonder who would bother even attempting to surmount them. The FDA itself expected that not many would try. The agency initially predicted that the costs would be "high enough to expect additional product exit, consolidation, and reduction in variety" and that only twenty to eighty applications would be received in the first two years of regulation.[47] (It has since revised this estimate upward.) This outcome was temporarily avoided when then FDA commissioner Scott Gottlieb delayed full implementation of the rules until 2022, temporarily staving off regulatory Ragnarok.[48] In July of 2019, however, a federal judge ordered the FDA to impose a deadline of just ten months for e-cigarette producers to submit product applications, throwing the future of the entire industry into doubt.[49] The FDA had not even released guidance explaining what to include in applications until the month before.[50] The costs and uncertainties inherent in compliance may be too much for small vapor companies to bear, driving out the independent businesses that built the market for vaping products from the bottom-up and clearing the field for only the largest and most well-funded companies, including those affiliated with Big Tobacco.[51]

The result of these decisions is that the United States no longer has a dynamic market for competitors to the cigarette. No new vaping products have been permitted for sale since the FDA's rules took effect, freezing the state of technology as it stood in late 2016. In October 2018, the FDA went further by announcing a ban on the sale of most flavored e-cigarettes in any retail outlet open to minors, a move that relegates them to specialty vapor shops and tobacconists. Juul was targeted with special scrutiny, and the company responded by removing nearly all of its flavors from in-person retail sales.[52] San Francisco banned the sale of e-cigarettes entirely until they receive FDA approval and other jurisdictions are likely to follow suit.[53] The perverse irony of these regulations is that many Americans can no longer buy vapor devices at a convenience store, but they can buy the perfectly lethal cigarettes that have been killing millions for more than a century. This completely backwards approach puts the most dangerous tobacco product within the easiest reach of consumers.

THE OPTIMISTIC CASE FOR E-CIGARETTES

Although there are open questions about the long-term effects of e-cigarette use, the conclusion that they are significantly safer than conventional cigarettes is widely accepted by health experts. In the United Kingdom, a comprehensive report by the Royal College of Physicians concluded that long-term vaping is unlikely to exceed 5% of the risk of smoking cigarettes.[54] The Cochrane Tobacco Addiction Review Group concurs that "switching to electronic cigarettes is likely to lead to significant improvements in health."[55] Even the American Cancer Society concedes that individuals who do not quit smoking by other means "should be encouraged to switch to the least harmful form of tobacco product possible."[56] Researchers are still developing a complete picture of e-cigarettes' overall impact, but it is no longer in any serious doubt that smokers switching to vaping will greatly reduce their exposure to the harmful compounds produced by burning tobacco.

None of this is to say that using e-cigarettes is completely safe or that it is inappropriate to urge caution about using them, especially for teenagers and nonsmokers who might be inclined to take them up. There are legitimate questions surrounding who uses the products, what the long-term effects might be, how useful they are as an aid to quitting, and how efforts at harm reduction will play out at the population level. It's too soon to answer all of these questions with complete certainty. Conventional cigarettes have been studied for nearly a century, and in that time their basic design has, aside from the addition of the filter tip, changed fairly little. E-cigarettes have seen significant use for little more than a decade and their designs are rapidly evolving. It would be foolish to attempt answers that are too precise. We can, however, sketch out the contours of what we know so far — and what we know provides good reasons to be optimistic about e-cigarettes for both individual smokers and public health in general.

The question of whether e-cigarettes are effective as a cessation aid is one of the most contentious debates in tobacco control. Cigarette smokers who have converted to vaping often evangelize about its amazing potential to help others quit, but anecdotal claims need to be backed up by unbiased data. The ideal way to address this question is through randomized control trials. Those that have been completed suggest that e-cigarettes compare very favorably to typical nicotine replacement therapies such as gums or patches. A study with nearly 900 participants published in the *New England Journal of Medicine* found that smokers provided with e-cigarettes successfully abstained from smoking at almost twice the rate of smokers given pharmaceutical nicotine replacement therapies.[57]

Observational studies provide additional evidence that e-cigarettes are effective at aiding cessation. The most notable of these, a 2017 study in the *British Medical Journal*, examined cross-sectional data from a survey of more than 20,000 American smokers. It found that half of recent quitters had tried e-cigarettes and that e-cigarette users were both more likely than non-users to attempt quitting and more likely to succeed. Most importantly, the study determined that the population-level cessation rate declined, too. The authors conclude that this "is the kind of data pattern that has been predicted but not observed at the population level for cessation medication... This is the first statistically significant increase observed in population smoking cessation among US adults in the past fifteen years."[58] Similarly, survey data from 19,000 British smokers attempting to quit revealed that e-cigarettes offered the highest odds of success of all cessation aids, with users nearly twice as likely to remain abstinent from cigarettes one year later than those making unaided quit attempts.[59]

The counterargument to this is that vaping maintains addiction to nicotine rather than weaning smokers entirely, which may lead to sustained dual-use in which people vape some of the time and smoke real tobacco on other occasions.[60] Although dual-use is obviously less healthy than complete cessation of smoking, reducing the frequency of smoking is still beneficial. "There's an all-or-nothing mentality," says Michael Siegel, who advocates tobacco harm reduction from his position at the Boston University School of Public Health, "but there's no question that reducing smoking improves health, especially for lung cancer and respiratory diseases, for which there's a dose-response relationship."[61] (Cardiac risks accrue at lower levels of exposure and so would be less affected by reduced smoking, though there could be benefits here, too, if dual-users only rarely indulge in actual tobacco.)

Taken as a whole, the evidence points to e-cigarettes being useful as a cessation aid. One of their biggest advantages is that smokers are eager to try them. "Whatever we think of the evidence on their effectiveness, smokers are choosing to use e-cigarettes much more widely than other available forms, such as nicotine patches and nicotine-containing gums," says Professor John Newton of Public Health England. "There is no doubt that they are popular among smokers. The first step to being an effective aid is that they have to be used by smokers. That is very much in their favour."[62]

Opposite the question of cessation is initiation. Who takes

up vaping, and does doing so put them on a path to smoking? The most pressing question here regards youth uptake of vapor products. The fear is that teenagers will get addicted to nicotine and — more worrisome — that this addiction will lead them to cigarettes.

Youth vaping became a huge issue in 2018 when the FDA declared it an "epidemic."[63] Health officials released only a fraction of current data, however, and did so in a way that seemed to deliberately exaggerate the true scale of the problem. A report from the CDC stated that "overall tobacco product use increased by 38 percent among high school students."[64] That sounds alarming, but it's also misleading to lump all forms of tobacco into one figure; it would be more accurate to refer to this grouping as "nicotine products" since e-cigarettes don't contain tobacco. The overall statistic doesn't provide any information about which type of nicotine products students are using or how often they're using them, even though occasional or experimental vaping has radically different health implications than habitual smoking. By omitting this crucial information, the CDC's statistic obscured as much as it illuminated.

The number of students who reported using an e-cigarette at least once in the past thirty days did increase sharply, rising from 11.7% to 20.8%. This is obviously concerning, but the more relevant figure is the proportion of high school students who use e-cigarettes on a regular basis, defined in the survey as on twenty or more of the past thirty days. Only about 5.8% of high school students reported frequently vaping, and many of these students were also using more harmful tobacco products. Ideally, of course, high schoolers would abstain from nicotine entirely. Realistically, there's no way to provide access to safer forms of nicotine for adults that won't have at least some spillover to youth. From a public health perspective, smoking tobacco is much more worrisome than vaping. The FDA, CDC, and various anti-smoking organizations have warned for years that e-cigarettes will act as a gateway drug by addicting teenagers to nicotine and renormalizing smoking. Years of data suggest that this isn't happening to any great degree. Cigarette use among American high schoolers has fallen by half in less than a decade, from 15.8% in the 2011 National Youth Tobacco Survey to 8.1% in 2018.[65] This is the same period in which the popularity of vaping rose substantially, undermining the scary narrative that e-cigarettes are seducing kids into smoking.

Evidence from England also suggests that the widespread availability of e-cigarettes is not leading to frequent use by youth, especially among teenagers who have never smoked.[66] Future trends could force a re-appraisal, but so far it appears that vaping is more likely to be a substitute for smoking than a gateway. (Some studies find that students who vape are also more likely to smoke, but this may simply reflect the fact that young people who engage in one risky behavior are more likely to engage in others. Discerning the causality of alleged gateway effects is notoriously difficult.)[67]

Similar patterns hold for adult e-cigarette users. The percentage of American adults who smoke declined from 19% in 2011[68] to 14% in 2017.[69] Dr. Brad Rodu, who holds an endowed chair in tobacco harm reduction research at the University of Louisville, draws on CDC data to conclude that as of 2018 there were more than three million ex-smokers who are currently vaping.[70] It would be inaccurate to credit all of this success to e-cigarettes, but at the very least it's clear that their widespread use is compatible with significant declines in smoking.

Use of e-cigarettes is concentrated among current or former smokers, although the proportion of never smokers who report vaping at least occasionally has increased. From a public health perspective, the ideal scenario is for no nonsmokers to ever experiment with e-cigarettes. But e-cigarettes can benefit public health even if patterns of use fall short of this ideal. Researchers evaluate this by what they refer to as the "risk/use equilibrium." This is a way of estimating how many nonsmokers would have to take up vaping to offset the gains of smokers or potential smokers switching to less harmful products.[71]

This equilibrium depends on the ratio of risk between vaping and smoking. If vaping carries 20% of the risk of smoking, for example, five nonsmokers would have to take up vaping to offset the gains of one cigarette smoker switching. If vaping carries 5% of the risk — the estimate of some health authorities — then twenty nonsmokers would have to take up vaping to offset the gains of one smoker switching. If the latter estimate is correct and if e-cigarettes are even somewhat effective at preventing people from smoking, then a whole lot of nonsmokers would have to start vaping for the technology to be harmful at the population level.

A recent study published in *Tobacco Control* lends further weight to the idea that e-cigarettes will promote beneficial health outcomes. Researchers modeled optimistic and pessimistic scenarios surrounding vaping in the United States. The pessimistic scenario assumes that e-cigarettes are more harmful than currently thought, that many people who have never smoked will take them up, that vaping will act as a gateway to smoking, and that residual smoking rates will hover around 10%. Yet both scenarios still end up predicting big improvements over the status quo. The optimistic scenario suggests that vaping could prevent 6.6 million premature deaths and eighty-six million lost years of life between now and

2100. The pessimistic scenario still predicts the prevention of 1.6 million premature deaths and twenty million lost years of life. In other words, even if the pessimists are right, e-cigarettes are likely to be a life-saving technology.[72]

Much more research is required to fully map out the effects that the disruptive technology of e-cigarettes will have on public health, and there is always the possibility of unpleasant surprises. Given sometimes conflicting science, a pessimist could offer a more negative assessment than I have given here. Open questions about the long-term effects of vaping on respiratory and circulatory systems will take years to fully resolve. Regulators, lawmakers, and health groups cite these unknowns as reasons to restrict the use of e-cigarettes. But there is also danger in being too risk-averse. A report from the Royal College of Physicians warns that an overly precautionary approach may result in missed opportunities to reduce smoking. "[If] this approach also makes e-cigarettes less easily accessible, less palatable or acceptable, more expensive, less consumer friendly or pharmacologically less effective, or inhibits innovation and development of new and improved products, then it causes harm by perpetuating smoking. Getting this balance right is difficult."[73]

Striking the right balance is made even more difficult by ideological divides within the tobacco research community. As mentioned at the beginning of this chapter, opposition to vaping is only partially explained by empirical uncertainty. Health activists' hostility can only be fully understood within the context of a decades-long campaign to stigmatize smoking and achieve a society completely free of nicotine, no matter the desires of individual users.

. . .

MORAL PANIC CLOUDS THE DEBATE

From the very beginning, e-cigarettes were intended to help people quit smoking. As their designs have evolved and they have become increasingly popular, a growing body of evidence suggests that they act as a substitute for combustible tobacco and help people quit, smoke less often, or never take up smoking in the first place. Yet despite these benefits, public perception of vaping has become increasingly fear-driven. Press coverage often does more to hype alarm about e-cigarettes than to communicate their potential benefits for public health. Use by young people is a particularly fraught topic in news stories. "Malia Obama puffing her Juul is summer goals," read one extremely 2018 headline.[74] The popularity of Juul among students proved to be an enduring story, culminating with then commissioner of the FDA Scott Gottlieb's proclamation of an epidemic. Gottlieb lamented that concern over youth use "puts the entire opportunity at risk for adult smokers" and warned that if trends don't reverse, "the consensus supporting these products for adults will disappear."[75]

Press coverage that conveys accurate information about how e-cigs can play a role as a lower-risk alternative to cigarettes is comparatively rare. As a result, the public is remarkably uninformed about the differences between smoking and vaping.[76] In a 2016 survey, nearly 80% of American respondents agreed with the false statement that nicotine is the primary disease-causing agent in tobacco.[77] A Rasmussen poll from August of 2018 found that more than 60% of Americans believe that e-cigarettes are as dangerous or more dangerous than smoking cigarettes.[78] National surveys reveal that the American public's beliefs about e-cigarettes have become increasingly inaccurate over time.[79] These mistaken beliefs are most prevalent in older Americans; a recent Gallup report found that almost half of seniors sixty-five and older believe that vaping is "very harmful to health," in contrast to only 22% of adults under thirty.[80] Another dispiriting poll found that 45% of adult smokers, the group that would benefit most from an accurate understanding of the relative risks, still believes that vaping and smoking are comparably dangerous.[81]

Health authorities, anti-smoking activists, and journalists all share in the blame for misinforming the public. Stories that irresponsibly exaggerate the risks of vaping abound, but it's worth noting a few particularly egregious examples. In a 2013 article for the *Daily Beast*, a columnist wrote about his experience switching from cigarettes to vaping. Instead of viewing this as a success, a doctor from the Mayo Clinic led him to conclude that he was "likely inhaling Chinese-made antifreeze."[82] That same year, the director of the University of North Carolina's Tobacco Dependence Program claimed on television that e-cigarette vapor "could be several thousand degrees when it hits your lungs," a fact that would make vaping instantaneously lethal if it were remotely true.[83] In 2015 the *New England Journal of Medicine* tweeted that vaping could carry a "higher cancer risk than smoking," an absurdly out-of-context projection that was picked up in news stories all around the world.[84] Viral reports in 2016 warned that vaping causes "popcorn lung," a rare respiratory disease associated with workers in popcorn factories but not with vaping.[85] In 2018 headlines proclaimed that vaping doubles the risk of heart attack, even though this finding is methodologically dubious.[86] That same year, another prominent researcher compared e-cigarettes to "bioterrorism."[87] In 2019, the FDA stoked fears that e-cigarettes cause seizures despite lacking evidence of a causal connection,[88] and journalists on the Public Broadcasting Service produced a segment suggesting that youth vaping is likely to be a gateway to crack and heroin.[89]

In an unintentionally revealing blog post, the American Lung Association recently stated that "scientists have been working hard to debunk the belief that e-cigarettes are less harmful than traditional cigarettes."[90] The relative safety of e-cigarettes is supported by a strong consensus, but it's true that some researchers in professional tobacco control seem ideologically committed to finding evidence of the opposite. Some of the most frightening allegations made against e-cigarettes originate from researchers with a long history of anti-smoking alarmism. The assertion that vaping doubles the risk of heart attack came from Dr. Stanton Glantz, of Helena heart miracle notoriety, and subsequent research suggests that his recent work is similarly flawed.[91] The "bioterrorism" comparison was credited to Jonathan Winickoff, the same physician who made headlines a decade earlier by associating fear and stigma with the new concept of thirdhand smoke; Winickoff now also warns against the dangers of thirdhand vapor.[92]

These exaggerated attacks are frightening both the public and policymakers, undermining efforts to promote tobacco harm reduction. The barrage of misinformation is further exacerbated by FDA regulations that forbid e-cigarette companies from communicating truthful statements about their products to consumers. Without explicit approval from the FDA, they may not advertise that their products are lower-risk than cigarettes, that they contain fewer harmful constituents, that switching to e-cigarettes may be beneficial to health, or that they may aid in quitting or reducing smoking. Although commercial speech is less protected than political speech, the FDA's restrictions are arguably so restrictive that they violate the First Amendment.[93]

As evidenced by the public's misperceptions of e-cigarette risks and the rising tide of anti-vaping legislation, better communication is desperately needed to protect e-cigarettes from oppressive regulation. Health authorities are not rising to the challenge. Former FDA commissioner Scott Gottlieb, for example, began his term with promises to embrace new technologies for harm reduction. Yet he seemed persistently incapable of advocating forcefully on behalf of adult vapers, worsening a difficult state of affairs by failing to make a compelling case for e-cigarettes. As a result, the FDA has abetted the spread of alarmism about their dangers and their use by teens.

Of course, regulators can and should take steps to restrict youth access to e-cigarettes, particularly through enforcement at the retail level, and they are justified in noting that the long-term effects of e-cigarette use require further study. But the more challenging task before them is to temper the climate of fear that now surrounds vaping. The thirty-four million Americans who continue to smoke and the politicians responding to moral panic need accurate information. They are unlikely to receive it from traditional anti-smoking groups, many of whom oppose nicotine consumption by any means, regardless of the level of risk. In a blog post criticizing his peers in tobacco control and exposing anti-smoking groups that make false statements about the risks of vaping, Michael Siegel writes that the movement "has largely abandoned truth as a central value." He continues:

> Driven by an almost puritanical inability to accept the fact that
> a person could obtain pleasure from nicotine without it killing
> them, we have made the demonization of vaping the solitary
> goal of the movement, at the direct expense of what I always

believed was our primary goal: to make smoking history. [...] We simply cannot tolerate the fact that there are millions of adults who are deriving pleasure from, and improving their health because of, the use of a much safer form of nicotine delivery. The problem with vaping is that it is *not* killing anyone, so there is no punishment for the vice of being addicted to nicotine. And that's something that the tobacco control movement can simply not tolerate.[94]

LOOKING BEYOND PUBLIC HEALTH

In most debates about e-cigarettes, the products are evaluated purely by their potential to help smokers quit and thereby benefit public health at the population level. Even by that stringent standard, anti-smoking activists should have ample reason to support them. But many vapers find e-cigarettes appealing for reasons that the public health framing fails to capture; to look exclusively at cessation studies and population health effects is to treat e-cigarettes as if they are just another pharmaceutical device. That's not the way vapers themselves view them. Sarah Jakes of the New Nicotine Alliance eloquently explained the disparity in her keynote remarks at an e-cigarette conference in 2017:

The word "pleasure" seems to be something of an anathema to some in public health. One of the biggest challenges for consumers is in getting regulators, and those who advise them, to understand that for a great many people vaping is not a medicine, or simply a smoking cessation intervention, it works precisely because it isn't those things. It works because they enjoy it. They love the personalization that's made possible by the diversity of the market in devices, and the thousands of flavours available. They enjoy the identity of being a vaper and the sense of community that that entails. They love that vaping is similar to smoking, but at the same time a million miles away from it.[95]

More than anything else, what distinguishes e-cigarettes from other nicotine replacement therapies is that vaping can be pleasurable and fun. Patches and gums are boring, officially approved, handed down from the sterile hallways of Glaxo-SmithKline and the Food and Drug Administration to fix something that's wrong with people. E-cigarettes give them something to enjoy. This is precisely what makes anti-smoking activists so uncomfortable. The judgment against vaping is motivated more by aesthetics than its opponents will ever admit.

For decades, the goal of anti-smoking activists has been to define smoking as an antisocial act. Previous chapters have shown how thoroughly they succeeded. As a result, it is now virtually impossible to have a debate about e-cigarettes that respects adult choices. One of the most striking aspects of various proposals to ban e-cigarettes or restrict vaping in public is the complete absence of any pause to question whether government ought to be interfering in these decisions of consenting adults. After decades of stigmatization, it's become almost unthinkable to suggest that we should respect the preferences of adult nicotine users in the same way that we respect the preferences of adult drinkers and, increasingly, adult marijuana users. It's not just that the preferences of smokers and vapers lose out in a cost-benefit analysis. It's that their preferences are never taken seriously at all.

The innovations that are making safer nicotine consumption possible arrived in a time of cultural realignment with regard to the use of various psychoactive substances. University of London historian Virginia Berridge has noted that western societies are increasingly willing to distinguish between "use" and "problem use" for cannabis and some other illegal drugs, but any use of tobacco is viewed as inherently problematic. "Tobacco was changing places to become more like a drug, while drug use itself was becoming 'normalized' and part of a wide spectrum of substance use in society," writes Berridge in her 2013 book *Demons*, which tracks attitudes toward alcohol, tobacco, and drugs from the early 19th century to the present day. "From the 1980s onward, new ideas about drug use tended to see it as more 'normal' while tobacco smoking became seen as pathological."[96]

These attitudes are so pervasive that they are threatening the most promising product ever devised for tobacco harm reduction, forcing vapor advocates into a defensive posture couched in purely medical terms. And while the harm reduction case for e-cigarettes is compelling, I'd like to suggest a more radical proposal for how we should approach regulation: Recognize adults' ownership of their own bodies. Regard vaping not as mere medicine (it's more than that) or just another form of smoking (it's much safer), and treat it as one of many moderately risky activities that consenting adults should be free to engage in.

When it comes to other legal drugs, we don't require that products intended for adults be made unpalatable to minors, even if they're not supposed to be getting their hands on them. Teen drinking is a serious problem in the United States — the CDC estimates that excessive drinking causes more than 4,300 deaths among the underaged each year[97] — but we don't address this by banning adult beverages that young people also find appealing. In states that have legalized cannabis, a visit to any pot dispensary will dispense with the notion that sweet and fruity flavors are just for kids; plenty of middle-aged adults line up for edibles in flavors like "Fruity Krispy Treat" or "Citrus Dreamsicle." Some of this stuff eventually makes its way to minors, but more than 60% of the U.S. agrees that legalizing it is better than filling prisons with peaceful marijuana users.[98]

Yet when it comes to nicotine, policymakers, health activists, and journalists seem incapable of treating anyone as a free adult. One might be tempted to dismiss objections to vaping restrictions as fodder for perpetually grumbling libertarians, but the failure to adequately defend the interests of people who use e-cigarettes is putting real lives at risk. Vaping has the potential to help millions of adults quit smoking. For that to happen, they need accurate information about the lower risks of e-cigarettes, liberty to use them, and access to flavors and formats that make them more appealing than real tobacco. Restrictions contemplated by Congress, the FDA, and state and local governments will undermine this goal.

Globally, the need for tobacco harm reduction is even more urgent. The lethal toll of the cigarette epidemic is gradually shifting from wealthy countries to the developing world. Within a decade, three-quarters of the deaths caused by tobacco will likely occur in developing countries.[99] Yet in many of them, safer products like snus and e-cigarettes are forbidden or simply unavailable. In the West, too, vulnerable populations such as the poor, the mentally ill, and the incarcerated are ill-served by public health strategies that rely on stigma, taxation, and behavioral control.[100] Paternalist policies that deny these groups access to safer alternatives consign them to lives of continued smoking.

More than thirty-four million American adults currently

smoke. Around ten million use e-cigarettes. To avoid the mistakes of previous prohibitions and drug wars, it's necessary to recognize these people not as pathological addicts but as equal citizens. As with other dangerous substances, that still allows a productive role for government. Lawmakers and regulators can ensure that nicotine products work as advertised, set limits on toxic chemicals in vapor, tax products in proportion to their harm, and fund educational campaigns about the dangers of smoking. They can provide accurate information about the lower risks of vaping to the smokers who need to hear it most. And, of course, they can step up enforcement against underage sales, which the current rise in teen vaping shows is clearly needed. Other interventions should be off-limits, however, and lawmakers and anti-smoking crusaders will have to tolerate that some people will vape for pleasure, including many who were never smokers.

Nicotine and tobacco use will probably always be with us in some form, legal or not. We can, in a liberal society, take reasonable steps to discourage that use while allowing smokers and vapers the freedom to purchase the products they prefer and giving them truthful information about the risks and harms of each. All of that begins with respecting the right of consenting adults to make their own decisions — and not using the panic over teenage use to justify treating an entire nation like children.

The electronic cigarette may turn out to be the most significant innovation in the nicotine market since the Bonsack machine automated cigarette rolling in the 1880s. Vaping arose while mainstream tobacco control activists obsessed over trivial ideas like changing the colors of cigarette packaging; that it arose at all is thanks to a decade of permissionless innovation before the FDA could say, as it has done now, "Stop." The story of successful tobacco harm reduction is a story of people in power not getting their way. Nicotine, however, has been subverting the desires of the powerful since the Spanish Inquisition. As we'll see in the final chapter, the role of pleasure and the question of who decides what adults may do with their own bodies is inescapably central to ongoing debates about nicotine and tobacco.

* * *

ADDENDUM: AS THIS BOOK GOES TO PRESS IN SEPTEMBER OF 2019, the United States is gripped by panic over vaping. Mysterious lung illnesses have appeared, teen use rose for another year, and the FDA announced its intent to ban flavored e-cigarettes nationwide. Emerging evidence suggests that the illnesses are mostly linked to cannabis products, though the causes are not yet known with certainty. In the long-run, I suspect that these incidents will reveal more about drug policy than they do about e-cigarettes, although it is a reminder that we do not yet know everything we need to know about vaping. Regardless, the damage has been done. Anti-smoking groups and politicians took advantage of the crisis to push bans through, with the likely effects of driving some vapers back to smoking, creating a black market, exacerbating misperceptions of e-cigarettes, and advantaging products owned by tobacco companies. In the midst of all this, one encouraging fact has been almost completely ignored: Preliminary figures show the youth smoking rate falling to another record low, down from 8.1% to 5.8% in just one year.[101]

ENDGAME

Nothing ever ends.
　— Alan Moore, *Watchmen.*[1]

TOWARD THE END OF 2018, I celebrated the tenth anniversary of my move from Arlington, Virginia, to the more bohemian Portland, Oregon, with a glass of Scotch, a large cigar, and the company of a good friend. As our conversation turned to tobacco laws and the creeping regulations dictating where and what Americans are permitted to smoke, my friend posed a question: In another ten years, would the evening we'd just enjoyed still be legal in the United States? Would cigars survive another decade of anti-smoking activism, or would we be forced to score them on the black market or sneak them back in luggage on trips abroad? As outlandish as that prospect may seem, it's not far-fetched to worry that cigars and every other form of combustible tobacco will be banned from sale, at least in the forms we know them.

This outcome once seemed unthinkable, but many anti-smoking groups believe that this goal is now within reach. Advocates of so-called "endgame" strategies want to bring an end to smoking and are willing to employ coercive means to do so. Although the precise definition of what constitutes a successful endgame is up for debate, it's generally understood to mean the near or total elimination of combustible tobacco. Radical proposals for achieving this include requiring a license to purchase it, limiting and gradually reducing the supply until it reaches zero, and outright prohibiting its sale.[2]

The endgame strategy most likely to come into play in the United States is mandating the removal of nicotine from cigarettes. The idea is to make the level so low that no one will become addicted and to force current smokers to seek the drug from less harmful sources. But as noted in the chapter on Bootleggers and Baptists, any rule of this nature would very likely expand beyond its initial scope. The prospect of cigarette smokers shifting their consumption to cigar and pipe tobacco, paired with pressure from anti-smoking groups and for-profit companies that would benefit from eliminating competition, would eventually lead the Food and Drug Administration to extend the rule to combustible tobacco in all its forms. Traditional products that have been enjoyed since before the arrival of Columbus would be rendered effectively illegal. In combination with the FDA's pre-market review process and strict regulation of e-cigarettes, this will complete a total federal takeover of the American market for tobacco and nicotine.

That prospect reflects the extensive powers now possessed by public health regulators. More than that, it reflects a significant shift in ideas. The standard framing of contemporary debates within tobacco control pits advocates of pragmatic harm reduction against abstinence-only hardliners. On the surface, the two camps are in tension, and the debates between them are as heated as any in academia. But as American tobacco policy advances toward a potential endgame, this framing fails to capture a more fundamental disagreement. The newly salient division is between those who embrace a liberal approach to regulation and those who advocate aggressively technocratic central planning. The liberals want to see the market for cigarettes eroded by voluntary means, with smokers choosing for themselves to quit or take up lower-risk alternatives like e-cigarettes or snus; liberals support empowering consumers by expanding the range of choices and providing accurate information about the risks of each. The technocrats seek not to nudge, but to shove, controlling the market from the top-down by banning some products entirely and coercively rendering others less appealing. If the technocrats prevail, the freedom to smoke or use nicotine in any form may be extinguished.[3]

TECHNOCRACY VS. DYNAMISM

The illiberal advocates of the tobacco endgame are united by the belief that their preferred vision ought to be imposed from the top-down via legislation or government agencies. This technocratic approach is fearful of bottom-up evolution and tolerates change only when it's tightly managed by the right authorities. As Virginia Postrel describes technocracy in her insightful 1998 book *The Future and Its Enemies*, "Technocrats are 'for the future,' but only if someone is in charge of making it turn out to plan." That there must be a plan is never questioned: "The issue isn't *whether* the future should be molded to fit one static ideal. It's what that static ideal should be. There must be a single blueprint for everyone."[4]

Technocrats insist upon a "one best way" determined by experts. Postrel argues instead for an approach that she calls "dynamism." Dynamists are open to a future that unfolds in unpredictable ways, recognizing the limited knowledge of human beings and the differing values of diverse individuals. Dynamists "permit many visions and accept competing dreams... Their 'central organizing principle' is not a specific outcome but an open-ended process. A dynamic future tolerates diversity, evolves through trial and error, and contains a rich ecology of human choices."[5]

Snus, e-cigarettes, and other products that some health authorities now view as essential for tobacco harm reduction owe their evolution to precisely this kind of dynamic process. They arose from the bottom-up in response to consumer-driven selective pressures. The development of e-cigarettes is a textbook example of "creative destruction," economist Joseph Schumpeter's wonderfully potent phrase describing innovation in capitalist economies. This relentless process "revolutionizes the economic structure *from within*, incessantly destroying the old one, incessantly creating a new one." The rise of the cigarette in the late nineteenth and early twentieth centuries was one such period of creative destruction, with old ways of making and consuming tobacco giving way to the new. The current period is another, as conventional cigarette companies lose ground to unforeseen competitors inventing safer ways of delivering nicotine. Schumpeter would have recognized the "gale of creative destruction" at work.[6]

The profits of cigarette companies and the planning of anti-tobacco technocrats are both threatened by such unpredictable innovation, and both groups use the power of the state to contain it. The previous two chapters documented the means by which Big Tobacco has become adept at manipulating regulations to protect itself from competition and technological change. Regulators, too, have restricted the use of novel nicotine products. Snus was treated by health officials in Sweden and Norway with what could generously be described as benign neglect; the prospect of selling it outside of Scandinavia met with outright hostility and a ban throughout the European Union.[7] The FDA's first response to e-cigarettes in the United States was an attempt to forbid their import.[8] Both products have now established successful records of harm reduction, but given the opportunity, technocrats would have banned them before they ever had the chance to prove their worth.

Regulatory gatekeepers and endgame advocates are wary of allowing adults to make informed choices about nicotine and smoking. They react with fear to the popularity of vaping because it challenges the "triple goal" of the anti-smoking movement: "to end the death and disease caused by tobacco, to end nicotine addiction and to destroy the tobacco industry."[9] The rise of e-cigarettes challenges the unity of these aims, advancing the first while potentially leaving the latter two unfulfilled. The fierce opposition to vaping must be understood by the ways in which it upsets this static vision of the future.

The activist wings of tobacco control are populated by the kind of professionals whom the liberal economist Friedrich Hayek described as "the single-minded idealists." They do not like being caught off guard. Many of them have spent their entire careers working to end the use of nicotine and tobacco. But as Hayek notes, technocrats' priorities are not always shared by the people they govern. Their plans are "the result not of a comprehensive view of society but rather of a very limited view and often the result of great exaggeration of the ends they place foremost." When they exercise political power, they allow their own desires to override those of their fellow citizens. This, Hayek warns, makes the very people "who are most anxious to plan society the most dangerous if they were allowed to do so — and the most intolerant of the planning of others."[10]

The most difficult case to make to technocrats is that they should relinquish control and embrace an open-ended tomorrow. Karl Lund of the Norwegian Institute of Public Health argues that much of the hostility to harm reduction arises from the fact that consumers are choosing products that evolved outside of the medical regulatory framework, developed not by pharmaceutical conglomerates or government agencies, but by Silicon Valley start-ups, strip mall vape stores, and sometimes the dreaded Big Tobacco companies. "I think much of the opposition… comes from the fact that [the] health side has been on the outside," says Lund. "These innovative products have emerged without their control and approval… It is difficult for us to realize and accept that these products may have greater potential to make smoking obsolete than the regulations many of us have spent a lifetime fighting for."[11]

Future debates over tobacco will be defined by this conflict between technocratic planning and dynamic evolution. This is another way of saying that the conflict will be between authority and liberty. The path favored by contemporary tobacco control will lead inevitably to more restrictions on consenting adults. The open-ended, optimistic nature of the liberal vision will allow for a richer array of choices.

THE DENIAL OF PLEASURE AND THE PATH TO PROHIBITION

"Alongside the discourses of harm and addiction that dominate both tobacco control and tobacco harm reduction, there must also be a place for pleasure," writes anthropologist Kirsten Bell, whose research critically examines the relationship between the field of professional tobacco control and the smokers it supposedly seeks to help. She poses a provocative question: "What, if we were to take pleasure seriously, might tobacco control and tobacco harm reduction actually look like?"[12]

Some harm reduction advocates who acknowledge the benefits of smokers switching to lower-risk alternatives dread the prospect of nonsmokers using those same products for pleasure; they even threaten to ban them if that occurs. But if these products are effective, the population of habitual smokers will fade away as they switch, quit, or never initiate the habit. As these gains are realized, the underlying questions of consent and coercion that have always surrounded tobacco use are bound to come roaring back. What happens to the small minority of people who continue smoking cigarettes in spite of everything? What about those who smoke occasionally for pleasure, perhaps with cigars or pipes? What about nonsmokers who take up snus or vaping? We'll inevitably have to confront the fact that people are smoking or consuming nicotine and the question of what, if anything, to do about it.

Mitch Zeller, director of the FDA's Center for Tobacco Products, raised similar questions in an article published in *Nicotine and Tobacco Research*. "How comfortable are we with long-term, or possibly permanent, use of less harmful nicotine delivery mechanisms by adults," Zeller asks, "if they help keep currently addicted smokers from relapsing to combustible tobacco products?"[13] To which a liberal might reply, "Who is the relevant 'we' and why should their determination of what is comfortable be decisive for everyone else?" One struggles to find any indication in the statements of public health authorities that the preferences of individual smokers or vapers are viewed as a constraint on their actions. Vaping becomes, at best, a lesser sin to be tolerated as a means of preventing the mortal sin of smoking; consumption of nicotine may be justified medically but never recreationally.

That people might *want* to smoke or vape is held to be irrelevant. Indeed, on occasions when government economists have attempted to account for smokers' lost pleasure in cost-benefit analyses of proposed regulations, they have been rebuked by activists and academics who argue that smoking is so irrational that smokers' foregone enjoyment is not worth weighing.[14] This sterile worldview paves the way to increasingly authoritarian interventions, including total prohibition.

In the eyes of the most extreme endgame advocates, nicotine itself is the enemy, not the harms associated with its inhalation via cigarettes. Many therefore dismiss the idea of helping smokers by allowing them access to safer ways of taking the drug. They accuse snus and vaping of being nothing more than sneaky ways of sustaining addiction. "Talk of 'safer cigarettes' is rather like talking about safer terrorism, or safer smallpox, or safer forms of drowning," writes tobacco historian Robert Proctor, completely rejecting the potential benefits of harm reduction.[15] Such comparisons ignore that while many smokers urgently wish to quit because of health dangers and social stigma, they do derive some pleasure from the practice. Peter Hajek, a tobacco researcher at the Wolfson Institute in London, sums up the Puritanical anti-nicotine mindset: "Better to keep smokers smoking and dying than to allow them to have their fun without the risk."[16]

Proctor, the most vocal advocate for tobacco prohibition, explicitly denies that tobacco can be a recreational drug like alcohol or marijuana and contends that banning it would therefore be uncomplicated, "requiring (in theory) nothing more than the stroke of a pen."[17] He argues that "Prohibition [of alcohol] failed because most people who drink actually like it and can do so responsibly, whereas virtually all tobacco use is abuse."[18] Most smokers "do not enjoy it; they smoke because it relieves their cravings."[19] This argument would not go over well in any cigar lounge, or among many cigarette smokers for that matter. The first cigarette smoker I explained it to responded with derisive laughter and bluntly declared, "That's bullshit." While acknowledging the reality of addiction and the dangers of smoking, he waxed rhapsodically on the exquisite pleasure of the day's first cigarette paired with his morning coffee. Although it's painfully true that many smokers regret their habit and wish to quit, the casual denial that smoking offers them anything at all erases the complexity of their experiences.

Proctor's sole nod to smokers' desires is an allowance that they may "grow, cure, and smoke whatever kinds of substances they like, for personal or noncommercial use."[20] The impracticality of that exception betrays the lack of seriousness with which he regards smokers' own preferences. Of what use is the freedom to grow one's own tobacco to a person living in a small apartment or an unsuitable climate? For those who can pull off the trick of growing, curing, and rolling their own tobacco, what chance do they have of making anything comparable to the products of commercial firms with decades of accumulated expertise? Cigar smokers in Portland, New York, or Los Angeles can hardly be expected to match the standards of professionals in Nicaragua, Honduras, or Havana. If they managed to produce anything at all, the reduction in quality and variety would still be a significant loss. (Proctor has himself struggled to grow tobacco at his home in California, an experience that apparently has not given him any sympathy for smokers he would force into the same futile effort.)[21]

Prohibition of tobacco would not work out nearly as easily as its advocates suggest. The freedom to exchange for things we cannot produce ourselves is among the most essential liberties, and when it is infringed people find ways of working around the barriers. Historically, smokers have continued lighting up even at the risk of execution. Personal and noncommercial tobacco growers would not stay small for long; today's high taxes already incentivize illegal trade and prohibition would encourage it even more. That wouldn't be stopped with the peaceful stroke of a pen. Governments would have to choose between tolerating black markets or cracking down on buyers and sellers, inviting the same privacy invasions, state-sanctioned violence, and mass incarceration that have long accompanied the War on Drugs. How many of us would endorse such a step, especially at a time when we are finally recognizing the folly of doing so for plants like marijuana?

Supporters of prohibition dodge such questions by denying that smokers possess any freedoms to be meaningfully infringed. Smokers hate their habit so intensely, they suggest, that prohibitionists would be greeted as liberators. Proctor prefers the term "abolition" to "prohibition," adapting the language of the anti-slavery movement to the cause of banning tobacco. Legislators in Hawaii echoed this doublespeak in a bill to raise the minimum age for purchasing cigarettes to 100: "Banning the sales of cigarettes should be viewed as a good faith effort to free smokers from the enslavement of this powerful addiction and not an infringement on individual liberties."[22]

Because they do not take smokers' liberties seriously, there is no limiting principle to what endgame advocates may do to force smokers to abstain. Yet many smokers will, and successfully have, quit solely due to persuasion. In the previous century, popular reporting about the risks of cigarettes and the landmark Surgeon General's report of 1964 motivated many smokers to give up the habit, initiating the long-term decline in American smoking rates. Taxes, location-based restrictions, anti-smoking ad campaigns, bans on sales to youth and marketing to minors, warnings on cigarette packs, and the disapproval of friends and family members nudged others to quit or never begin smoking. By these means, the rate of smoking in the United States declined by more than half since its peak in the 1960s, when more than 40% of the adult population smoked, to less than 15% today.[23]

Now we face the question of what to do with the last holdouts, currently about a sixth of the American population. How do endgame advocates respond when persuasion, taxes, and smoking bans aren't enough? The answer, if abstinence is the only acceptable aim and pleasure is illegitimate, is to keep tightening the screws. The extremists in tobacco control don't just ban smoking in indoor public spaces; they ban it everywhere. They don't just worry about secondhand smoke; they accuse smokers themselves of literally emitting toxins. They don't tax tobacco reasonably; they tax it exorbitantly. They don't stop at putting written warnings on cigarette packs; they force smokers to gaze upon grotesque medical imagery every time they buy them. They don't encourage smokers to switch to lower-risk products; they demonize them and forbid their sale. In short, they make it miserable to be a smoker, and the message they convey to smokers is that they are stupid, sick, stigmatized, and unwelcome in society.

The anti-smoking movement began with well-intentioned

efforts to help people quit smoking, to prevent them from taking up the habit, and to change social norms that invited smokers to foul the air wherever they pleased. It has morphed into an ideological crusade. Today's anti-smoking activists deny the agency of consenting adults, abridging their rights to smoke together in privately owned spaces or to purchase products that drastically reduce their exposure to lethal carcinogens. They no longer recognize the dignity of smokers and other nicotine users as equal citizens with the right to decide what goes into their own bodies. They have become profoundly illiberal.

Against the endgame

Although endgame advocates portray their aim as a new approach to tobacco control, it's in fact a very old vision. The likes of King James and Murad the Cruel shared it, the latter going to extreme lengths to earn his moniker. Lucy Page Gaston, the early twentieth century cigarette prohibitionist, campaigned for "A Smokeless America by 1925."[24] Surgeon General C. Everett Koop shifted the goalposts to "a smoke-free society by the year 2000."[25] Three years after that deadline passed, Surgeon General Richard Carmona made his own intentions explicit in testimony before Congress: "I see no need for any tobacco products in society."[26] The dream of a smoke-free society is perpetually one generation away. King James eventually realized it was better to tax tobacco than to ban it. Murad's name was revived ironically as a brand of cigarettes.[27] Page survived to see the year 1925 pass by with millions of Americans still puffing away, as did Koop in 2000. Carmona ended up joining the board of an e-cigarette company.[28]

Although today's endgame advocates differ in some respects from their historical predecessors, they share the belief that their vision of a smoke-free future ought to be achieved by force. They are convinced that the modern regulatory state empowers them to finally succeed where so many before them have failed. Their unquestioned assumption is that the desire for a smoke-free society is universally shared. As endgame advocate Kenneth Warner has written in the journal *Tobacco Control*, "While we struggle today with often widely divergent perspectives and beliefs, we all share the same vision of the final words to this story: 'The end.'"[29] That may be true among Warner's peers in public health, but it's a self-serving illusion to pretend that it extends to society writ large. Anti-smoking activists too often forget that the aim of a liberal society is to give people space to pursue their own ends, not to insist that they conform to others'. Their limited worldview allows no room for dissent. They may view smoking as a vice, an addiction, or a disease, but never as a pleasure or genuine choice. They refuse to concede that anyone could have defensible reasons for smoking.

Even among some advocates of harm reduction, viewing every kind of nicotine use through the lens of addiction leads to an absurdly simple understanding of how and why people consume it. Their vision of the endgame reduces centuries of complex cultural behavior to the mechanical pursuit of a single chemical in the bloodstream, as if the experience is equally satisfying whether delivered via a boring dermal patch, a mass-produced cigarette, a mango-flavored Juul, or a hand-rolled cigar aged in cedar. By pretending that the only relevant differences between these products are their health effects, they deceive themselves into believing that they can ban some and allow others without imposing significant costs on the people who enjoy them.

Equally simplistically, they sort everyone into the binary

categories of "smoker" or "abstainer." Among the smokers, it doesn't matter how frequently they light up, what type of tobacco they prefer, or how deeply they inhale. For some endgame advocates, it does not even matter whether they inhale smoke or mere vapor. They are all smokers, full stop. In contrast, a humane liberal approach would recognize that people have diverse preferences when it comes to tobacco and nicotine. It would not demand a false divide between virtuous abstainers and sinful smokers. In place of the Manichean moralizing of today's anti-smoking movement, I suggest a more diverse taxonomy that recognizes a richer variety of experiences:

Abstainers — They never smoke or use nicotine, or they did so in the past and have now quit.

Habitual smokers — They smoke frequently and are likely addicted to nicotine. Most of them primarily smoke cigarettes, but they may be addicted to tobacco in other forms.

Occasional smokers — They smoke infrequently and don't suffer addiction to nicotine; they could take it or leave it if they wanted to. They smoke mostly cigars, pipes, or other less common forms of tobacco, but also include the "chippers" who enjoy cigarettes on social occasions without feeling compelled to have them all the time. They consume tobacco primarily for pleasure.

Nonsmoking nicotine consumers — They consume nicotine in ways that are significantly safer than combustible tobacco. These include snus, e-cigarettes, and potentially heat-not-burn tobacco. They may use these products as a less harmful way of managing nicotine dependence or simply because they enjoy them or find them useful.

Thinking in terms of these four groups is a less reductive, more flexible, and accurate taxonomy. Reducing the number of habitual smokers can remain an aim of public policy, but in this view there are three groups into which those smokers may transition, not just one. Habitual smokers can be enticed with a suite of better options instead of being confronted with ever more hostility and infringements on their freedom.

Options are the hallmark of a liberal approach, which respects some constraints on the means used to reduce the prevalence of smoking. Past some point, the coercion of adults is simply unacceptable. Whereas anti-smoking activism has become authoritarian, technocratic, and exclusively devoted to its own ends, our approach to smoking in a free society should be liberal, dynamist, and tolerant of dissenting preferences. This approach differs from contemporary tobacco control in important areas of policy, sketched below.

Harm reduction — Cigarette smokers should be allowed and encouraged to try safer forms of nicotine delivery. The public is misinformed about the relative safety of e-cigarettes due to fear-driven campaigns by anti-smoking activists, government agencies, and alarmist media. The risks of nicotine use should be accurately communicated; snus and e-cigarette producers should be freed from speech restrictions that forbid them from advertising truthful statements to consumers. Flavor bans that inhibit these products' ability to compete with conventional cigarettes should be repealed. Other traditional anti-smoking measures should account for the relative safety of these products so that policies do not discourage their use by current or potential smokers.

Innovation — Producers of nicotine and tobacco products should have clear ideas of what will be allowed for sale, and the FDA should replace its onerous, opaque, and costly process of pre-market review with objective, transparent standards. Products that do not involve significant design changes should not require expensive, time-consuming review. This is especially true for well-established categories like cigars, cigarettes, and pipe tobacco, products which rarely raise new questions of health. Standards for e-cigarettes should focus on minimizing toxic chemicals and ensuring safe operation while allowing consumers to experiment with different flavors, components, and concentrations of nicotine. Approval of new products should not be contingent upon bringing about a predetermined pattern of use at the population level; the aim should be to ensure that individual consumers have the accurate information they need to make informed, personal decisions about products advertised truthfully in an open, competitive market.

Smoking bans — Contemporary smoking bans far exceed any reasonable response to the risks of secondhand smoke. This is not to suggest that exposure is without risk. The extent of today's bans, however, is driven by ideologically motivated science that grossly exaggerates it. Outdoor bans should mostly be repealed, with smoking policies left to the discretion of individual venue owners. Indoor bans should be amended to ensure that business owners who wish to cater to smokers can take reasonable steps to do so. Exemptions should be permitted not just for businesses that have been arbitrarily grandfathered in, but for new entrants, too. These exemptions should not be class-based, favoring high-end cigars over other products like cigarettes or hookah; all forms of smoking should be treated equally, respecting all people's rights to social spaces.

Taxes — Taxes on tobacco are generally sufficient to cover the external costs of smoking in the United States. Enthusiasm for additional tobacco taxes should be tempered by the fact that smokers tend to be among the least well-off in society, making increases highly regressive. Taxes on products such as e-cigarettes and snus should account for their lower risks to encourage switching.

Sales restrictions — Reasonable steps may be taken to limit the sale of tobacco, especially with the aim of preventing addiction among youth. Limiting sales via licensing or raising the age of purchase, approaches that are already standard for alcohol, are potential means of accomplishing this goal. Full prohibition, however, would restrict liberties, encourage black markets, and invite violence by state authorities and illegal dealers. Adults should be free to purchase tobacco, including flavored products that are currently forbidden. Sales restrictions should not make combustible tobacco more accessible than safer nicotine alternatives, a perverse outcome currently proposed or enacted in various jurisdictions.

Respect for smokers and nicotine users — The noble aim of reducing the harms of smoking is no excuse for treating smokers without dignity. Contemporary tobacco control stigmatizes smoking, denies that there is any value to the practice, and looks down upon smokers as ignorant, toxic addicts incapable of acting in their own interests. Anti-smoking measures should be constrained by respect for the choices of consenting adults, recognizing their individual autonomy.

In contrast to the authoritarians of contemporary tobacco control, liberals aim to empower smokers by allowing a market for safer products to flourish. We respect the rights of adults to choose what goes into their bodies, whether it be a pack a day of cigarettes, a regular hit off a vape pen, or a cigar on special occasions. We wish to save lives and prevent disease but also to preserve freedom. We are justifiably optimistic that cigarette use will continue to decline, but do not claim to know the single best way to persuade habitual smokers to quit. Nor do we demand that our vision be imposed from above by technocratic central planners. We accept and embrace that patterns of nicotine and tobacco use will be determined from the bottom-up, reflecting the choices of millions of diverse individuals, and tolerate that this pattern may differ from our own preferences. Our endgame is a game that never ends, a future that continues to surprise.

CONCLUSION

Only that which can change can continue.
— James P. Carse, *Finite and Infinite Games*[1]

2019 IS a challenging time to be taking up the cause of smokers' rights. Respect for smoking and smokers is at a nadir. "Tobacco, finally, is becoming a losers' drug," observed historian David Courtwright at the beginning of the century, noting a decline in social status that has only accelerated since then.[2] Even the tobacco companies aren't up to the task of defending cigarettes anymore. Philip Morris now boasts of "designing a smoke-free future," betting on lower-risk alternatives to keep the revenue flowing as cigarette sales continue their downward spiral.[3] One doesn't need to believe that Big Tobacco has adopted altruistic motives to recognize a substantial shift in attitude from when the companies were utterly shameless in their denials of cigarettes' dangers and willing to fight tooth and nail against any limits on smoking. Today, when the smokers' rights movement inspires any notice at all, it's as an anachronistic and powerless curiosity. A 2015 profile of the New York-based group CLASH — that's Citizens Lobbying Against Smoker Harassment — casually dismissed the group's arguments as not even worth debunking: "The war is over, the smoke has cleared. The odds that CLASH or any other group will roll back Bloomberg's policies are close to non-existent."[4]

The extent to which defenders of smokers' rights have faded into cultural irrelevance is illustrated in the contrast between two novels set a couple decades apart. Christopher Buckley's satirical *Thank You for Smoking*, published in 1994, drew its inspiration from that era's slick spokesmen for Big Tobacco. The protagonist is Nick Naylor, representative of the Academy of Tobacco Studies and paid shill for the pre-Master Settlement Agreement cigarette industry. Naylor is young and handsome, earns a six-figure salary, drives a BMW, flies in a private jet, and appears on Oprah and Larry King. He earns his keep by denying the risks of smoking and deftly shifting the terms of debate to everything from the intrusive nanny state to the dangers of nuclear weapons.[5] The portrayal is funny because it was true, but it's no criticism of the book to say that Naylor's character now seems remarkably dated. The lucrative role of brazen cigarette shill and the America he inhabited no longer exist.

Twenty-two years later, the smokers' rights movement shrinks to a punchline in Nell Zink's 2016 comic novel *Nicotine*. Featuring a cast of millennial squatters occupying dilapidated houses in New Jersey, Zink's story is only tangentially about smoking. The squatters in each property devote themselves to a progressive cause such as environmentalism, AIDS, or disarmament. Then there's the Nicotine house, a collection of impoverished misfits united by their grumpiness over smoking bans and cigarette taxes. "Nicotine's kind of an outlier… because it's the catchall house, with activists working on all different fronts," explains one of the residents. "But we do have this one thing in common that gets us ostracized at every single march and rally and everywhere we go. That's how we ended up banding together."[6] That one thing is the use of tobacco. Secondhand smoke gets the Nicotine residents pushed out to the fringes of every progressive rally. "It's because they're good leftists," declares another resident. "They want to blame perpetrators, not victims. And everybody is the smokers' victim." No one in the novel takes the cause of smokers' rights quite seriously, least of all the residents of Nicotine. It's funny because it's true.

But smokers' rights deserve to be taken seriously. By failing to do so, we treat smokers as less than equal citizens and do them harm. Through my own experience of becoming a smoker, I've come to know people like publican Don Younger who saw the community he nurtured for decades at the Horse Brass ground beneath the heel of public health bureaucracy. I've met smokers who are unfailingly polite to the nonsmokers around them but who resent being stigmatized and denied any spaces at all in which to light up. I've encountered makers of pipes and cigars who worry that they are too small to survive under regulations designed for, and often supported by, Big Tobacco. And through the passionate online community of vaping enthusiasts, I've been introduced to countless former smokers and vape shop owners who struggle to make their voices heard by the lawmakers and health authorities who put their lives and livelihoods at risk.

Anti-smoking crusaders are so convinced of the righteousness of their cause that they dismiss the interests of smokers, vapers, and other nicotine users as unworthy of consideration. They view tobacco as pure vice and therefore cannot contemplate any loss in its disappearance. The people they seek to control know better. German writer and former smoker Gregor Hens explored the appeal of smoking in his memoir of overcoming addiction, also titled *Nicotine*, stretching from his first to his final cigarette. "I've smoked well over a hundred thousand cigarettes in my life, and each one of those cigarettes meant something to me. I even enjoyed a few of them," he quips in the opening lines, acknowledging the compulsive nature of addiction. Yet Hens never reduces his experience to the dreary maintenance of nicotine:

> I've smoked hastily, and other times slowly and with pleasure... I've smoked in 110 degree heat and in minus 15 cold, in libraries and seminar rooms, on ships and mountaintops, on the steps of Aztec pyramids, furtively in an old observatory, in basements and barns and beds and swimming pools, on air mattresses and in thin-hulled rubber dinghies, on the prime meridian in Greenwich and the 180th meridian in Fiji. I've smoked because I was full and I've smoked because I was hungry. I've smoked because I was glad and I've smoked because I was depressed. I've smoked out of loneliness and out of friendship, out of fear and out of exuberance. Every cigarette that I've ever smoked served a purpose – they were a signal, medication, a stimulant or a sedative, they were a plaything, an accessory, a fetish object, something to help pass the time, a memory aid, a communication tool or an object of meditation. Sometimes they were all of these things at once... I regret nothing. Every cigarette I've ever smoked was a good cigarette.[7]

The notion of a "good cigarette" is impossible to contemplate for those who understand tobacco only in terms of its effects on health, rendering its pleasures invisible. Cornell University professor of French literature Richard Klein knew better, too. He explored similar themes in his 1991 book *Cigarettes Are Sublime*, rejecting the purely negative perception of smoking for a far more nuanced appraisal:

> [Suppose], which is highly unlikely, that cigarette smoking were to vanish from America. Would anything be lost? If billions of people during nearly a hundred years have been taking uncounted puffs from trillions of cigarettes, there must be some advantage — at least a perceived one — in smoking. If smoking were to cease tomorrow, not only might something of utility be lost (although compensated by the enormous gain to general health), but a certain quality of experience that smoking made possible would be extinguished as well. Perhaps it is only at the moment that cigarette smoking vanishes that we can discover the place it occupies in our social imaginary — in the myths and the dreams, the consolation and the intensification, the intuitions and the charms to which it has given rise.[8]

Cigarettes Are Sublime is no endorsement of cigarettes. Klein uses "sublime" in its Kantian meaning, one in which the act of smoking is imbued with a particular kind of beauty that is inseparable from the awareness that each cigarette brings the smoker one step closer to death. "Kant calls 'sublime' that aesthetic satisfaction which includes as one of its moments a negative experience, a shock, a blockage, an intimation of mortality. It is in this very strict sense that Kant gives the term that the beauty of cigarettes may be considered to be sublime," explains Klein.[9] His book is an intentional exercise in hyperbole, an attempt at lavishing excessive praise on cigarettes as a corrective to their universal denigration: "The effort of imagination required to praise cigarettes way beyond their value allows one to measure the depths to which their value has fallen. To say that cigarettes are sublime installs a ratio that allows one to conclude that they are not simply abysmal."[10]

What Hens and Klein keenly appreciated, and what today's anti-smoking activists do not, is that smoking has never been pure vice. When smokers quit cigarettes, they really do surrender something of value. As Klein expresses it, "[The] act of giving up cigarettes should perhaps be approached not only as an affirmation of life but, because life is not merely existing, as an occasion for mourning. Stopping smoking, one must lament the loss to one's life of something — or someone! — immensely, intensely beautiful, must grieve for the passing of a star."[11]

Of course, nearly everyone now agrees that this sacrifice is worthwhile. Knowing what we do about the dangers of cigarettes, we should fervently wish for them to become a relic of the twentieth century. It will be cause for celebration if their use is extinguished — voluntarily, not by government fiat — as smokers give them up in pursuit of greater happiness. My hope is that innovations such as snus or vaping, along with some of the less invasive tools of tobacco control, will help make cigarettes a thing of the past in much the same way that the cigarette replaced snuff and chaw.

I believe that other forms of tobacco, however, are worth preserving. Discussions of smoking are so thoroughly enmeshed in the public health framing that it has become almost impossible to recognize that there is anything good about the practice. Although some forms of smoking are substantially less detrimental to health than others, none of them are affirmatively beneficial. It follows that there is no need for tobacco. Yet millions of people do see the need — not just the need, but the desire. Cigars and pipes are better than "not simply abysmal." By thinking exclusively of how to live longest, health activists ignore the more important question, "How to live?"

To take a fuller view of life is to consider the experiences that make life joyous. Can, and should, those experiences include smoking? It's a question with no universal answer. I smoke pipes and cigars only sparingly, and I encourage anyone who smokes them often to endeavor not to. Yet if I consider giving up smoking entirely, I recall conversations with friends and family sharing cigars and pipes, solitary walks and reveries enhanced by the aroma of tobacco smoke, celebrations marked with the lighting of stogies and the sipping of expensive rum or whiskey, and dates concluding with a romantic smoke nestled by the fire. By any honest accounting, my life has been enriched by the enjoyment of tobacco. To pretend otherwise would be a lie.

At the beginning of this book, I invited the reader to see tobacco with fresh eyes, as if it were an exotic and wondrous crop, not a poisonous commodity to be purchased in packs of twenty at any convenience store. What would tobacco look like if we were innocent of the cigarette? We would see a plant with intriguing flavors, a rich history, and a beguiling ability to suit our moods at seemingly contradictory occasions. We'd see a companion there for us when we honor a victory as well as when we mourn a loss. We'd see a means of adding texture to life. We'd see a product that's not for everyone, but is understandably for some.

Of course, observing the carnage inflicted by the cigarette in the twentieth century and continuing today, it's impossible to take such a rosy view of tobacco. The leaf's friends and foes alike should cheer the creative destruction of that exceptionally lethal and addictive product. But let's not forget that there is value in smoking, too. Having overcome my own anti-tobacco prejudice through the experience of smoking pipes and cigars, I've come to believe that it's an indulgence worth defending. Lost in discussions of the very real problem of how to reduce mortality is acknowledgment that tobacco does have redeeming qualities, that it can be enjoyed in moderation, and that not all forms of nicotine use are equally dangerous. We should aim not for a coercively achieved smoke-free society, but for a liberal society in which the harms of tobacco are minimized and consenting adults are free to make their own decisions about a plant that has entranced human beings for centuries. Going forward, many of us will gladly say farewell to smoking and nicotine entirely. Others will be drawn to safer ways of enjoying the drug. And some, perhaps, will take pleasure in a rediscovery of tobacco.

ACKNOWLEDGEMENTS

A project is a thing you start up, get excited about, get stuck on, lock horns with, and later, if you're proud and bold and humble and arrogant and very stubborn, you tackle all the loose ends and finish it. What usually follows is a postnatal bewildered phase, and then finally a feeling of serenity comes over you, and with that the sad realization that nothing has changed, and that in all likelihood nobody really cares about your work. Then comes a kind of peace, and after that, God knows how, the seed of curiosity for a new project sprouts in you.

— Laia Jufresa, *Umami*[1]

I've smoked only a handful of cigarettes in my life. My first was at a dive bar in protest of the Washington, DC, smoking ban. I had no desire to be a cigarette smoker, but with smoking indoors soon to be made illegal, lighting up appealed as a minor act of rebellion. Although I didn't keep smoking — not cigarettes, anyway — I did keep writing about it. I've been covering issues related to tobacco for well over a decade. My writing has been scattered in blog posts, op/eds, and articles, addressing smoking bans, FDA regulation, taxes, and harm reduction. *The Rediscovery of Tobacco* has given me the opportunity to at last bring all of these topics together in one place.

Some would say that smoking bans are a weird issue to devote one's energy to, especially in 2019 when the political fights are basically over. There are certainly more pressing matters of public policy in the world, and any ranking of the worst things governments do to people would list telling them where not to smoke toward the bottom. I readily concede that it's a niche topic. Yet in another sense, social attitudes toward tobacco are anything but niche: Seven million people are projected to die from tobacco use each year. Convincing these millions to quit *or switch* to lower-risk products is literally a matter of life or death. The latter of these options is threatened by widespread unwillingness to question the ideological biases of the anti-smoking movement and by society's pervasive stigma against the use of nicotine and tobacco. The fight for harm reduction is in many ways a continuation of the fight over smoking bans, as both ultimately come down to whether we respect the rights of consenting adults to do with their bodies what they will. By bringing these subjects together in one volume, I hope I've helped illuminate that continuity.

The genesis of this book was an article I wrote for *The Atlantic* in 2012 entitled "The Case Against a Smoke-Free America," which caught the attention of many people who hated it and at least one person who liked it. That person, Jud Laghi, became my literary agent. After successfully selling my first book, he suggested extending the argument of that article into another. Alas, although we assembled a good proposal, editors questioned whether enough smokers remained in the United States to make the book profitable. I latched onto the idea, however, and determined that if no one was willing to publish it, I would press ahead and do it myself. Free from the obligations of advances or deadlines, I took a (let's be kind and say) leisurely approach to writing. I often ignored the manuscript for months. Eventually friends stopped asking when the book was coming out. Realizing that the work was beginning to stretch on for an embarrassingly long time, in 2018 I made it my New Year's resolution to finally finish it. This turned out to be my resolution for 2019, too, at which point I finally followed through.

I don't know if anything will change in my life now, if anyone will care about my work, or if another a new project will be forthcoming (though I do have ideas…). I am relieved to finally have this one out. And as much as writing is a solitary endeavor, I could not have completed it alone. The support and encouragement of my parents and family, especially Marie Gerwin, was invaluable. I'm thankful to the many experts and other sources who tolerated my questions and helped me hack more deeply into thorny empirical weeds. Michael Siegel, Carrie Wade, Karl Lund, Lars Ramström, Geoffrey Kabat, Amelia Howard, Glen Whitman, and David Sley all lent valuable insights, information, or experiences. Close friends and family provided critical readings for which I am deeply grateful: Lynn Grier, Conor Friedersdorf, Courtney Knapp, Julian Reif, Chad Wilcox, and Jeremy Horpedahl. For feedback on individual chapters or the project in general, I thank Scott Barton, Joey Coon, Wendy Purnell, Tim Hedberg, Joshua Keltner, Matthew Brown, Walter Olson, and Jim McDonald. The online community of vapers, harm reduction advocates, reporters, blog commenters, and skeptics of government coercion has provided a constant stream of useful information: Charles Gardner, Michelle Minton, Guy Bentley, Gregory

Conley, Joseph Magero, Marewa Glover, Sarah Jackson, Colin Mendelsohn, Will Truman, Matthew Perrone, Clive Bates, Jeff Stier, and Michael McFadden, among others. (Apologies to anyone I've forgotten!) Librarians at the Multnomah County Library kindly helped me track down necessary resources. Maureen Ogle and Evan Rail offered guidance on the self-publishing process. My editors at various publications have also greatly improved my work, challenging assertions, strengthening arguments, and forcing me to cut down my ungodly word counts: Susan Matthews at *Slate*, Peter Suderman at *Reason*, and James Hamblin at *The Atlantic*. I'm thankful for the opportunity to write for them. Finally, Andrew Bohrer did an amazing job illustrating the cover, capturing the tone of the book perfectly and tolerating seemingly endless changes to the files.

The history in this book treads some familiar territory. I am no historian, so I relied heavily on works by Richard Kluger, Allan Brandt, Robert Proctor, Iain Gately, and Cassandra Tate for the historical chapters. Sander Gilman and Zhou Xun's edited volume *Smoke* was another invaluable resource. In tone and style, my book is most closely aligned with the tradition of Jacob Sullum's *For Your Own Good* and Christopher Snowdon's *Velvet Glove, Iron Fist*. Anyone interested in looking deeper into the anti-smoking movement should read them; both authors are cited specifically at various points in the text, but the influence of their work is evident throughout. *For Your Own Good* was published in 1998 and *Velvet Glove, Iron Fist* in 2009; perhaps the excesses of the anti-smoking movement are worth revisiting every decade or so. In the time since they wrote their books, there has been a great deal of new science to cover, the potential of tobacco harm reduction has matured substantially, and of course there have been plenty of new restrictions on smokers' rights. I hope my own contribution is a worthy addition to the lineage.

I have never been a habitual smoker, but I can relate to the feeling that certain activities feel incomplete when unaccompanied by specific habits. Coffee and writing are as inextricably linked for me as coffee and cigarettes are for others. Independent of the chemical effects of caffeine, my writing mindset is simply at its best when I am in my favorite coffee shops with a warm ceramic mug stationed to the right of my laptop. So I think it's worth acknowledging the Portland coffee shops where the vast majority of this book was written: Saint Simon, Heart, Ristretto Roasters, the Hoxton lobby, and my long-time home, the Albina Press. Thanks for letting me occupy space for longer than is necessarily profitable for you.

Speaking of profit, I should disclose what little I have made for my advocacy. It's an article of faith among anti-smoking advocates that anyone who questions their aims must be a shill for Big Tobacco. As evidence that this is my motivation, they seize on the fact that for a year in my twenties I worked at the Cato Institute in Washington, DC. Although the think tank did accept some tobacco funding at that time, it was a small percentage of their budget and the vast majority of my work had nothing to do with smoking. I worked in the media department, a job that involved hardly any original writing or research, and I published rarely under Cato affiliation. I'm proud of my time there, but it's absurd to suggest that this tenuous financial connection is guiding my writing more than a decade later. The point of being a shill, after all, is to make money, and even if one takes the accusation at face value, I stopped getting paid a long time ago. If I'm a shill, I'm a shill with exceedingly generous terms and terrible skill at contract negotiation.

The most realistic explanation for why I wrote this book is the simple, obvious, and true one: I find the subject interesting. If all the editors who declined to purchase my proposal are correct, then returning to work in the hospitality industry would have been a more lucrative use of my time than trying to sell a self-published book on esoteric areas of public policy. If maximizing profit was my goal, those countless hours in coffee shops would have been better spent making coffee, not buying it. This is a passion project. In any case, the arguments in the book stand or fall independently of its funders, of which, as I've said, there are none. Anyone who attempts to dismiss it as corrupt advocacy has no grounds for being taken seriously.

As a final acknowledgment, I'd like to express my appreciation for all the friends, family, and strangers I've shared a smoke with over the years. Many of you smoke too much, and I urge you to quit. But I've always valued our time together. We're a small and welcoming community with ever fewer places to go. My thanks and admiration go out to those who refuse to roll over for authority, preserving the last spaces in which we can enjoy each other's company.

NOTES

INTRODUCTION

1. Cited in Deirdre N. McCloskey, *The Bourgeois Virtues* (Chicago: The University of Chicago Press, 2006), 60.
2. Parts of this introduction are adapted from Jacob Grier, "The Case Against a Smoke-Free America," *The Atlantic*, December 19, 2012, https://www.theatlantic.com/health/archive/2012/12/the-case-against-a-smoke-free-america/266220/. © 2012 Jacob Grier, as first published on TheAtlantic.com.
3. "Overview List – Number of Smokefree and Other Tobacco-Related Laws," American Nonsmokers' Rights Foundation, last modified July 1, 2019, https://no-smoke.org/wp-content/uploads/pdf/mediaordlist.pdf.
4. University of California, San Francisco, "Public Smoking Ban Slashes Heart Attack Rate in Community," press release, April 2, 2003, https://web.archive.org/web/20040803111917/http://pub.ucsf.edu/today/cache/news/200304012.html.
5. Quoted in Coco Ballantyne, "What is Third-Hand Smoke? Is it Hazardous?," *Scientific American*, January 6, 2009, https://www.scientificamerican.com/article/what-is-third-hand-smoke/.
6. Quoted in Lynne Peeples, "Your nose knows: The invisible threat of 'thirdhand smoke,'" *The Huffington Post*, August 26, 2011, https://www.huffpost.com/entry/thirdhand-smoke-smoking-risks_n_938241.
7. Cited in Tanya Pollard, "The Pleasures and Perils of Smoking in Early Modern England," in *Smoke*, ed. Sander L. Gilman and Zhou Xun (London: Reaktion Books, 2004), 39.

1. FROM NEW WORLD TO OLD

1. Cited in Timothy Brook, "Smoking in Imperial China," in *Smoke*, ed. Sander L. Gilman and Zhou Xun (London: Reaktion Books, 2004), 84.
2. Reay Tannahill, *Food in History*, (New York: Three Rivers Press, 1988), 202-220.
3. Samuel Eliot Morison, *Journals and Other Documents on the Life of and Voyages of Christopher* Columbus, trans. and ed. Samuel Eliot Morison, (New York: The Heritage Press, 1963), 65-71.

4. Cited in Samuel Eliot Morison, *The European Discovery of America: The Northern Voyages*, (New York: Oxford University Press, 1971), 298.

5. Iain Gately, *Tobacco*, (New York: Grove Press, 2001), 4.

6. Gately, *Tobacco*, 3.

7. Gately, *Tobacco*, 4-10.

8. Jordan Goodman, *Tobacco in History*, (London: Routledge, 1993), 29.

9. Gately, *Tobacco*, 5-6.

10. Gately, *Tobacco*, 4-10.

11. Francis Robicsek, "Ritual Smoking in Central America," in *Smoke*, ed. Sander L. Gilman and Zhou Xun (London: Reaktion Books, 2004), 34.

12. Robicsek, "Ritual Smoking in Central America," 34.

13. Robicsek, "Ritual Smoking in Central America," 30-31.

14. Cited in Goodman, *Tobacco in History*, 34.

15. Gately, *Tobacco*, 13-19.

16. Goodman, *Tobacco in History*, 32-35.

17. Samuel Eliot Morison, *The European Discovery of America: The Southern Voyages*, (Oxford: Oxford University Press, 1974), 72.

18. Cited in Fernando Ortiz Fernandez, *Cuban Counterpoint*, trans. Harriet de Onis, (New York: Alfred A. Knopf, 1947), 109-110.

19. Cited in Gately, *Tobacco*, 26.

20. Cited in Eric Deschodt and Philippe Morane, *The Cigar*, (Koln: Konemann, 1998), 18.

21. Gately, *Tobacco*, 38.

22. Goodman, *Tobacco in History*, 44-45.

23. Gately, *Tobacco*, 39-40.

24. Gately, *Tobacco*, 43-47.

25. W. A. Penn, *The Soverane Herbe*, (London: Grant Richards, 1901), 61.

26. Gately, *Tobacco*, 47.

27. Goodman, *Tobacco in History*, 60-65.

28. Cited in Penn, *The Soverane Herbe*, 219-220.

29. Tanya Pollard, "The Pleasures and Perils of Smoking in Early Modern England," in *Smoke*, ed. Sander L. Gilman and Zhou Xun (London: Reaktion Books, 2004), 39-42.

30. James I, "A Counterblaste to Tobacco," 1604.

31. Gately, *Tobacco*, 74-75.

32. Simon Schama, *The Embarrassment of Riches*, (New York: Vintage Books, 1987), 189.

33. Schama, *The Embarrassment of Riches*, 193-197.

34. Gately, *Tobacco*, 85-86.

35. Penn, *The Soverane Herbe*, 35-38.

36. Rudi Matthee, "Tobacco in Iran," in *Smoke*, ed. Sander L. Gilman and Zhou Xun (London: Reaktion Books, 2004), 65-66.

37. Matthee, "Tobacco in Iran," 58-66.
38. P. Ram Manohar, "Smoking and Ayurvedic Medicine in India," in *Smoke*, ed. Sander L. Gilman and Zhou Xun (London: Reaktion Books, 2004), 68-75.
39. Allen F. Roberts, "Smoking in Sub-Saharan Africa," in *Smoke*, ed. Sander L. Gilman and Zhou Xun (London: Reaktion Books, 2004), 46-57.
40. Allan Kulikoff, *Tobacco and Slaves*, (Chapel Hill: The University of North Carolina Press), 39-44.
41. Timon Screech, "Tobacco in Edo Period Japan," in *Smoke*, ed. Sander L. Gilman and Zhou Xun (London: Reaktion Books, 2004), 92.
42. Barnabas Tatsuya Suzuki, "Tobacco Culture in Japan," in *Smoke*, ed. Sander L. Gilman and Zhou Xun (London: Reaktion Books, 2004), 78-80.
43. Screech, "Tobacco in Edo Period Japan," 94-96.
44. Brook, "Smoking in Imperial China," 84-85.
45. Gately, *Tobacco*, 130-131.
46. Gately, *Tobacco*, 173-175.
47. Cited in V. G. Kiernan, *Tobacco: A History*, (London: Hutchinson Radius, 1991), 57-58.
48. Royal College of Physicians, *Harm Reduction in Nicotine Addiction*, (London: Royal College of Physicians, 2007), 4.

2. FROM SMALL TOBACCO TO BIG

1. W. A. Penn, *The Soverane Herbe*, (London: Grant Richards, 1901), 199.
2. Georges Herment, *The Pipe*, trans. Arthur L. Hayward, (New York: Simon and Schuster, 1954), 97-102.
3. Richard Carleton Hacker, *The Ultimate Pipe Book, Second Edition*, (Beverly Hills: Autumngold Publishing, 1989), vii.
4. Mary Pilon, "The Latest Thing They're Smoking in Pipes on College Campuses? Tobacco," *The Wall Street Journal*, February 20, 2009, https://www.wsj.com/articles/SB123509294170728733.
5. Andrew Martin, "Among the Pipemen," *Granta*, no. 105 (Spring 2009): 57-58.
6. Wil Hylton, "Tobacco That's so Brooklyn but Made in Belgium," *The New York Times Magazine*, April 12, 2013, https://www.nytimes.com/2013/04/14/magazine/tobacco-thats-so-brooklyn-but-made-in-belgium.html.
7. Parts of this introduction are adapted from Jacob Grier, "The Case Against a Smoke-Free America," *The Atlantic*, December 19, 2012, https://www.theatlantic.com/health/archive/2012/12/the-case-against-a-smoke-free-america/266220/. © 2012 Jacob Grier, as first published on TheAtlantic.com.

8. John LeLand, "When Smoke Gets in Your Pies (and Other Delectables)," *The New York Times*, March 26, 2003, https://www.nytimes.com/2003/03/26/dining/when-smoke-gets-in-your-pies-and-other-delectables.html.

9. Allan M. Brandt, *The Cigarette Century*, (New York: Basic Books, 2007).

10. Richard Kluger, *Ashes to Ashes*, (New York: Alfred A. Knopf, 1996), 18-20.

11. Kluger, *Ashes to Ashes*, 20.

12. Kluger, *Ashes to Ashes*, 22-23.

13. Kluger, *Ashes to Ashes*, 22-23.

14. Leslie Hannah, "The Whig Fable of American Tobacco, 1895-1913," *The Journal of Economic History* 66, no. 1, (2006): 42-73.

15. Robert Proctor, *Golden Holocaust*, (Berkeley: University of California Press, 2011), 40.

16. Paul R. Johnson, *The Economics of the Tobacco Industry*, (New York: Praeger Publishers, 1984), 16.

17. Jordan Goodman, *Tobacco in History*, (London: Routledge, 1993), 231.

18. Kluger, *Ashes to Ashes*, 22-23.

19. Kluger, *Ashes to Ashes*, 26.

20. Brandt, *The Cigarette Century*, 38-41.

21. Hannah, "The Whig Fable of American Tobacco, 1895-1913," 43-46.

22. Cited in Brandt, *The Cigarette Century*, 510, n. 49.

23. Kluger, *Ashes to Ashes*, 5-6.

24. Johnson, *The Economics of the Tobacco Industry*, 7.

25. Proctor, *Golden Holocaust*, 34-35.

26. Kluger, *Ashes to Ashes*, 6-7.

27. Leslie Iversen, "Why Do We Smoke? The Physiology of Smoking," in *Smoke*, ed. Sander L. Gilman and Zhou Xun (London: Reaktion Books, 2004), 319-323.

28. David T. Courtwright, *Forces of Habit*, (Cambridge: Harvard University Press, 2001), 114-115.

29. Penn, *The Soverane Herbe*, 205.

30. Cited in Kluger, *Ashes to Ashes*, 62.

31. Kluger, *Ashes to Ashes*, 17.

32. Cited in Brandt, *The Cigarette Century*, 50-51.

33. Kluger, *Ashes to Ashes*, 61.

34. Cassandra Tate, *Cigarette Wars*, (Oxford: Oxford University Press, 1999), 75.

35. Brandt, *The Cigarette Century*, 51-54.

36. Proctor, *Golden Holocaust*, 44-45.

37. Kluger, *Ashes to Ashes*, 64.

38. The Contributors' Club, "Smoking," *The Atlantic Monthly*, Volume 117 (April 1916), 574.

39. Brandt, *The Cigarette Century*, 63-65.
40. Kluger, *Ashes to Ashes*, 74-79.
41. Goodman, *Tobacco in History*, 105-106.
42. Kluger, *Ashes to Ashes*, 65-66.
43. Brandt, *The Cigarette Century*, 54.
44. Brandt, *The Cigarette Century*, 54-55.
45. Kluger, *Ashes to Ashes*, 60-61.
46. Kluger, *Ashes to Ashes*, 77.
47. Proctor, *Golden Holocaust*, 67-68.
48. Kluger, *Ashes to Ashes*, 77-78.
49. Courtwright, *Forces of Habit*, 116.
50. Proctor, *Golden Holocaust*, 71-75.
51. Tate, *Cigarette Wars*, 17.
52. Gary A. Giovino, "Epidemiology of Tobacco Use in the United States," *Oncogene* 21, (October 2002), 7327.
53. *The Health Consequences of Smoking: Nicotine Addiction*, (Rockville, MD: U.S. Department of Health and Human Services, Public Health Service, Office of the Surgeon General, 1988).
54. Quoted in Martin Tolchin, "Surgeon General Asserts Smoking Is an Addiction," *The New York Times*, May 17, 1988, https://www.nytimes.com/1988/05/17/us/surgeon-general-asserts-smoking-is-an-addiction.html.
55. Jacob Sullum, *For Your Own Good*, (New York: The Free Press, 1998), 220-221.
56. Jacob Sullum, *Saying Yes*, (New York: Jeremy P. Tarcher/Penguin, 2003), 231.
57. Centers for Disease Control and Prevention, "Quitting Smoking," fact sheet, accessed August 28, 2019, https://www.cdc.gov/tobacco/data_statistics/fact_sheets/cessation/quitting/index.htm.
58. Gene M. Heyman, *Addiction*, (Cambridge: Harvard University Press, 2009), 144-147.
59. Heyman, *Addiction*, 147-149.
60. Matthew Hilton, "Smoking and Sociability," in *Smoke*, ed. Sander L. Gilman and Zhou Xun (London: Reaktion Books, 2004), 128.
61. David Krogh, *Smoking*, (New York: W. H. Freeman and Company, 1991), 53.
62. Krogh, *Smoking*, 29.
63. Krogh, *Smoking*, 29-33.
64. Neal L. Benowitz, "Nicotine Addiction," *The New England Journal of Medicine*, 362 (June 17, 2019), 2295-2303.
65. Krogh, *Smoking*, 33-35.
66. Benowitz, "Nicotine Addiction."

67. Krogh, *Smoking*, 50-56.

68. Royal College of Physicians, *Harm Reduction in Nicotine Addiction*, (London: Royal College of Physicians, 2007), 45.

69. Reuven Dar et al., "Craving to Smoke in Orthodox Jewish Smokers Who Abstain on the Sabbath: A Comparison to a Baseline and a Forced Abstinence Workday," *Psychopharmacology*, 183, (2005), 294-299.

70. Krogh, *Smoking*, 93-97.

71. Krogh, *Smoking*, 3.

72. Krogh, *Smoking*, 97.

73. Rachel Laudan, *Cuisine and Empire*, (Los Angeles: University of California Press, 2013), 350-352.

74. Michael Pollan, "Unhappy Meals," *The New York Times Magazine*, January 28, 2007, https://www.nytimes.com/2007/01/28/magazine/28nutritionism.t.html.

3. SMOKING GUN

1. Hudson Maxim, *The Christian Advocate*, January 7, 1909, 36.

2. Cassandra Tate, *Cigarette Wars*, (Oxford: Oxford University Press, 1999), 4-5.

3. Cited in Tate, *Cigarette Wars*, 125.

4. Tate, *Cigarette Wars*, 49.

5. Henry Ford, *The Case Against the Little White Slaver: Volumes I, II, III, and IV*, (Detroit: Henry Ford, 1914), 5.

6. Tate, *Cigarette Wars*, 49.

7. Richard Kluger, *Ashes to Ashes*, (New York: Alfred A. Knopf, 1996), 39, 67.

8. Tate, *Cigarette Wars*, 19-24.

9. Tate, *Cigarette Wars*, 139-145.

10. Kluger, *Ashes to Ashes*, 72.

11. Brandt, *The Cigarette Century*, 105.

12. Kluger, *Ashes to Ashes*, 109.

13. Cited in Robert Proctor, *Golden Holocaust*, (Berkeley: University of California Press, 2011), 57.

14. Kluger, *Ashes to Ashes*, 133.

15. Sharon Bertsch McGrayne, *The Theory that Would Not Die*, (New Haven: Yale University Press, 2011), 108.

16. Siddhartha Mukherjee, *The Emperor of All Maladies*, (New York: Scribner, 2010), 241-242.

17. Kluger, *Ashes to Ashes*, 134.

18. Robert N. Proctor, *The Nazi War on Cancer*, (Princeton: Princeton University Press, 1999).

19. Kluger, *Ashes to Ashes*, 134-136.
20. Ernest L. Wynder and Evarts A. Graham, "Tobacco Smoking as a Possible Etiologic Factor in Bronchiogenic Carcinoma," *The Journal of the American Medical Association*, 143, no. 4 (May 27, 1950): 329-336.
21. Richard Doll and A. Bradford Hill, "Smoking and Carcinoma of the Lung," *British Medical Journal*, 2, (September 30, 1950): 739-748.
22. Kluger, *Ashes to Ashes*, 145-148.
23. Richard Doll and A. Bradford Hill, "The Mortality of Doctors in Relation to Their Smoking Habits," *British Medical Journal*, 1, (June 26, 1954): 1451-1455.
24. E. Cuyler Hammond and Daniel Horn, "Smoking and Death Rates – Report on Forty-Four Months of Follow-Up of 187,783 Men," *Journal of the American Medical Association*, 166, no. 11 (March 15, 1958), 1294-1308.
25. Ben Christopher, "Why the Father of Modern Statistics Didn't Believe Smoking Caused Cancer," *Priceonomics*, September 21, 2016, https://priceonomics.com/why-the-father-of-modern-statistics-didnt-believe/.
26. Ernest L. Wynder, Evarts A. Graham and Adele B. Croninger, "Experimental Production of Carcinoma with Cigarette Tar," *Cancer Research*, 13, (December 1953): 855-864.
27. *Smoking and Health*, (Washington: United States Department of Health, 1964).
28. Beate Pesche et al., "Cigarette Smoking and Lung Cancer – Relative Risk Estimates for the Major Histological Types from a Pooled Analysis of Case-Control Studies," *International Journal of Cancer*, 131, no. 5 (November 2, 2011), 1210-1219.
29. "Tobacco-Related Mortality," Centers for Disease Control and Prevention, accessed May 20, 2019, https://www.cdc.gov/tobacco/data_statistics/fact_sheets/health_effects/tobacco_related_mortality/index.htm.
30. Brian Rostron, "Smoking-Attributable Mortality by Cause in the United States: Revising the CDC's Data and Estimates," *Nicotine and Tobacco Research*, 15, no. 1 (January, 2013): 238-246.
31. Brian D. Carter et al., "Smoking and Mortality: Beyond Established Causes," *The New England Journal of Medicine*, 372, (February 12, 2015): 631-640.
32. "Prevalence," The Tobacco Atlas, accessed May 10, 2019, https://tobaccoatlas.org/topic/prevalence/.
33. "Tobacco," Tobacco Fact Sheet, World Health Organization, last modified July 26, 2019, https://www.who.int/news-room/fact-sheets/detail/tobacco.
34. Geoffrey C. Kabat, *Hyping Health Risks*, (New York: Columbia University Press, 2008), 32-33.

35. Kabat, *Hyping Health Risks*, 33.

36. Peter N. Lee, Barbara A. Forey, and Katherine J. Coombs, "Systematic Review with Meta-Analysis of the Epidemiological Evidence in the 1900s Related Smoking to Lung Cancer," *BMC Cancer*, 12, no. 385 (September 3, 2012).

37. Allan Hackshaw et al., "Low Cigarette Consumption and Risk of Coronary Heart Disease and Stroke: Meta-Analysis of 141 Cohort Studies in 55 Study Reports," *The British Medical Journal*, 360 (January 24, 2018).

38. "Smoking Against Fog and Damp," *The Lancet* (January 25, 1879), 131.

39. Brian Palmer, "Cooking Up Cancer," *Slate*, January 22, 2014, https://slate.com/technology/2014/01/cancer-risk-from-grilled-meat-is-it-time-to-give-up-smoked-and-fried-foods.html.

40. Wynder and Graham, "Tobacco Smoking as a Possible Etiologic Factor in Bronchiogenic Carcinoma."

41. I.T. T. Higgins, C. M. Mahan, and E. L. Wynder, "Lung Cancer Among Pipe and Cigar Smokers," *Preventive Medicine*, 17 (1988), 116-128.

42. Carlos Iribarren et al., "Effect of Cigar Smoking on the Risk of Cardiovascular Disease, Chronic Obstructive Pulmonary Disease, and Cancer in Men," *The New England Journal of Medicine*, 340 (June 10, 1999), 1773-1780.

43. S. Jane Henley et al., "Association Between Exclusive Pipe Smoking and Mortality from Cancer and Other Diseases," *Journal of the National Cancer Institute*, 96, no. 11, (June 2, 2004), 853-861.

44. N.J.Wald and H.C. Watt, "Prospective Study of Effect of Switching from Cigarettes to Pipes or Cigars on Mortality from Three Diseases," *BMJ*, 314 (June 28, 1997), 1860-1863.

45. Cindy M. Chang et al., "Systematic Review of Cigar Smoking and All Cause and Smoking Related Mortality," *BMC Public Health*, 15, (April 24 2015).

46. National Cancer Institute, *Cigars: Health Effects and Trends* (Bethesda 1998), ii-iii.

47. Alan Desantis and Susan E. Morgan, "Sometimes a Cigar [Magazine] is More than Just a Cigar [Magazine]: Pro-Smoking Arguments in *Cigar Aficionado*, 1992-2000," *Health Communication*, 15, no. 4 (February 2003), 457-480.

48. Jiping Chen et al., "Biomarkers of Exposure Among U.S. Cigar Smokers: An Analysis of 1999-2012 National Health and Nutrition Examination Survey (NHANES) Data," *Cancer Epidemiology, Biomarkers & Prevention*, 23, no. 12 (December 2014), 2906-2015.

49. Department of Health and Human Services, "Patient Protection and Affordable Care Act; Health Insurance Market Rules; Rate Review; Final Rule," *Federal Register* 78, no. 39 (February 27, 2013): 13413-13414.

50. Renata Micha, Sarah K. Wallace, and Dariush Mozaffarian, "Red and Processed Meat Consumption and Risk of Incident Coronary Heart Disease, Stroke, and Diabetes: A Systematic Review and Meta-Analysis," *Circulation*, 121, no. 21 (June 2010), 2271-2283.

51. Frank B. Hu et al., "Prospective Study of Major Dietary Patterns and Risk of Coronary Heart Disease in Men," *The American Journal of Clinical Nutrition*, 72, no. 4 (October 2000), 912-921.

52. Hui Lee et al., "*SULT1A1* Arg213His Polymorphism, Smoked Meat, and Breast Cancer Risk: A Case-Control Study and Meta-Analysis," *DNA and Cell Biology*, 31, no. 5 (May 2012), 688-699.

53. V. Bagnardi et al., "Alcohol Consumption and Site-Specific Cancer Risk: A Comprehensive Dose-Response Meta-Analysis," *British Journal of Cancer*, 112, no. 3 (November 25, 2014), 580-593.

4. SECONDHAND NEWS

1. Jonathan Swift, *The Examiner*, no. 15 (November 2 to November 9, 1710), 2.

2. Parts of this chapter are adapted from Jacob Grier, "We Used Terrible Science to Justify Smoking Bans," *Slate*, February 13, 2017, https://slate.com/technology/2017/02/secondhand-smoke-isnt-as-bad-as-we-thought.html.

3. "Public Smoking Ban Slashes Heart Attack Rate in Community," University of California, San Francisco, April 2, 2003.

4. Rosemary Ellis, "The Secondhand Smoking Gun," *The New York Times*, October 15, 2003, https://www.nytimes.com/2003/10/15/opinion/the-secondhand-smoking-gun.html.

5. BBC, "Town Slashes Heart Attacks," BBC, April 1, 2003, http://news.bbc.co.uk/2/hi/health/2907431.stm.

6. John Harrington, "Helena Heart-Attack Study Gets Worldwide Attention," *Helena Independent Record*, April 6, 2003, https://helenair.com/news/opinion/helena-heart-attack-study-gets-worldwide-attention/article_61944240-9eea-581d-845a-4ea8213ff2d9.html.

7. Michael Siegel, "Is the Tobacco Control Movement Misrepresenting the Acute Cardiovascular Health Effects of Secondhand Smoke Exposure? An Analysis of the Scientific Evidence and Commentary on the Implications for Tobacco Control and Public Health Practice," *Epidemiological Perspectives and Innovations*, 4, no. 12, (October 10, 2007).

8. Quoted in Michael Siegel, "Challenge Issued to Association of Nonsmokers - Minnesota to Retract Fallacious Claim and Apologize; Similar Challenge Issued to ClearWay Minnesota," *The Rest of the Story*,

November 28, 2006, https://tobaccoanalysis.blogspot.com/2006/11/challenge-issued-to-association-of.html.

9. Richard P. Sargent, Robert M. Shepard, and Stanton A. Glantz, "Reduced Incidence of Admissions for Myocardial Infarction Associated with Public Smoking Ban: Before and After Study," *BMJ*, 328 (April 24, 2004), 977-980.

10. Geoffrey Kabat, "When Effects Look Too Good to Be True, They Probably Are," *BMJ*, 328 (June 5, 2004), 1379.

11. RN Alsever et al., "Reduced Hospitalizations for Acute Myocardial Infarction After Implementation of a Smoke-Free Ordinance – City of Pueblo, Colorado, 2002-2006," *Morbidity and Mortality Weekly Report*, January 2, 2009, https://www.cdc.gov/mmwr/preview/mmwrhtml/mm5751a1.htm.

12. Sadik A. Khuder et al., "The Impact of a Smoking Ban on Hospital Admissions for Coronary Heart Disease," *Preventive Medicine*, 45, no. 1 (July 2007), 3-8.

13. Dong-Chul Seo and Mohammad R. Torabi, "Reduced Admissions for Acute Myocardial Infarction Associated with a Public Smoking Ban: Matched Control Study," *Journal of Drug Education*, 3, no. 3 (September 1, 2007), 217-226.

14. Francesco Barone-Adesi et al., "Short-term Effects of Italian Smoking Regulation on Rates of Hospital Admission for Acute Myocardial Infarction," *European Heart Journal*, 27 (2006), 2468-2472.

15. Michelle Sims et al., "Short-Term Impact of Smoke-Free Legislation in England: Retrospective Analysis of Hospital Admissions for Acute Myocardial Infarction," *BMJ*, 340 (June 8, 2010), 1-8.

16. Christopher Snowdon, "Latest Smoking Ban/Heart Attack Study Is Pure Junk Science," *Velvet Glove, Iron Fist*, June 9, 2010, https://velvetgloveironfist.blogspot.com/2010/06/latest-smoking-banheart-attack-study-is.html.

17. Institute of Medicine, *Secondhand Smoke Exposure and Cardiovascular Effects: Making Sense of the Evidence* (Washington, DC: The National Academies Press, 2010).

18. Pam Belluck, "Smoking Bans Reduce Heart Attacks and Disease," *The New York Times*, October 15, 2009, https://www.nytimes.com/2009/10/16/science/16smoke.html.

19. New Zealand Ministry of Health, *After the Smoke Has Cleared: Evaluation of a New Smokefree Law*, (Wellington: Ministry of Health, 2006), 97-103.

20. Kanaka D. Shetty et al., "Changes in U.S. Hospitalization and Mortality Rates Following Smoking Bans," *Journal of Policy Analysis and Management*, 30, no. 1 (November 11, 2010), 6-28.

21. Brad Rodu, "Acute Myocardial Infarction Mortality Before and After

State-Wide Smoking Bans," *Journal of Community Health*, 37, no. 2, (April 2012), 468-472.

22. Paul Basel et al., "The Effect of a Statewide Smoking Ordinance on Acute Myocardial Infarction Rates," *The American Journal of Medicine*, 127, no. 1 (January 2014), 94e1-94e6.

23. Vivian Ho et al., "A Nationwide Assessment of the Association of Smoking Bans and Cigarette Taxes with Hospitalizations for Acute Myocardial Infarction, Heart Failure, and Pneumonia," *Medical Care Research and Review*, 74, no. 6 (September 12, 2016), 687-704.

24. Mark W. Vander Weg, Gary E. Rosenthal, and Mary Vaughan Sarrazin, "Smoking Bans Linked to Lower Hospitalizations for Heart Attacks and Lung Disease Among Medicare Beneficiaries," *Health Affairs*, 31, no. 12 (December 2012), 2699-2707.

25. Hualiang Lin et al., "The Effects of Smoke-Free Legislation on Acute Myocardial Infarction: A Systematic Review and Meta-Analysis," *BMC Public Health*, 13, no. 529 (2013).

26. Stanton A. Glantz, "Why the Data in Latest Study on Smoke Free Laws and Heart Attacks Supports an Effect," University of California San Francisco Center for Tobacco Control Research and Education, October 1, 2016, https://tobacco.ucsf.edu/why-data-latest-study-smoke-free-laws-and-heart-attacks-supports-effect.

27. Cited in Ronald Bayer and James Colgrove, "Science, Politics, and Ideology in the Campaign Against Environmental Tobacco Smoke," *American Journal of Public Health*, 92, no. 6 (June 2002), 949.

28. Stanton A. Glantz, "Achieving a Smokefree Society," *Circulation*, 76, no. 4 (October 1987), 750.

29. Christopher Snowdon, *Velvet Glove, Iron Fist*, (Yorkshire: Little Dice, 2009), 140.

30. Takeshi Hirayama, "Non-Smoking Wives of Heavy Smokers Have a Higher Risk of Lung Cancer: A Study from Japan," *BMJ*, 282 (January 17, 1981), 183-185.

31. Dimitrios Trichopoulos et al., "Lung Cancer and Passive Smoking," *International Journal of Cancer*, 27, no. 1, (January 15, 1981), 1-4.

32. Elizabeth T. H. Fontham, Pelayo Correa, and Peggy Reynolds, "Environmental Tobacco Smoke and Lung Cancer in Nonsmoking Women," *Journal of the American Medical Association*, 271 (June 8, 1994), 1752-1759.

33. A. H. Wu-Williams et al., "Lung Cancer Among Women in North-East China," *British Journal of Cancer*, 62, no. 6, (December 1990), 982-987.

34. Snowdon, *Velvet Glove, Iron Fist*, 367-388.

35. *The Health Consequences of Involuntary Smoking: A Report of the Surgeon General*, Rockville, Maryland: U.S. Department of Health and Human Services, Office of the Surgeon General, 1986.

36. Kluger, *Ashes to Ashes*, 503-504.
37. Flue-Cured Tobacco Co-Op. v. U.S.E.P.A., 4 F. Supp. 2d 435, United States District Court for the Middle District of North Carolina, July 17, 1998, Justia.
38. Flue-Cured Tobacco Co-Op. v. U.S.E.P.A., July 17, 1998, Justia.
39. Flue-Cured Tobacco v. U.S.E.P.A., 313 F.3d 852, United States Court of Appeals, Fourth Circuit, December 11, 2002, Casetext.
40. Geoffrey C. Kabat, *Hyping Health Risks*, (New York: Columbia University Press, 2008), 168-171.
41. James E. Enstrom and Geoffrey C. Kabat, "Environmental Tobacco Smoke and Tobacco Related Mortality in a Prospective Study of Californians, 1960-98," *British Medical Journal*, 326 (May 17, 2003).
42. Geoffrey C. Kabat, *Hyping Health Risks*, (New York: Columbia University Press, 2008), 168-174.
43. Alison Tonks, "Passive Smoking: Summary of Rapid Responses," *British Medical Journal*, 327, (August 30, 2003), 505.
44. Sheldon Ungar and Dennis Bray, "Silencing Science: Partisanship and the Career of a Publication Disputing the Dangers of Secondhand Smoke," *Public Understanding of Science*, 14, no. 1 (2005), 12.
45. Virginia Berridge, "Passive Smoking and Its Pre-History in Britain: Policy Speaks to Science?," *Social Science and Medicine*, 49 (1999), 1183-1195.
46. Lawrence Gostin, "The Legal Regulation of Smoking (And Smokers)," in *Morality and Health*, ed. Allan M. Brandt and Paul Rosin (New York: Routledge, 1997), 346.
47. *The Health Consequences of Involuntary Exposure to Tobacco Smoke: A Report of the Surgeon General*, (Atlanta: United States Department of Health and Human Services, 2006).
48. *The Health Consequences of Involuntary Exposure to Tobacco Smoke: A Report of the Surgeon General*, Table 7.4.
49. Ange Wang et al., "Active and Passive Smoking in Relation to Lung Cancer Incidence in the Women's Health Initiative Observational Study Prospective Cohort," *Annals of Oncology*, 26, no. 1 (January 2015), 221-230.
50. Quoted in Judy Peres, "No Clear Link Between Passive Smoking and Lung Cancer," *Journal of the National Cancer Institute*, 105, no. 24 (December 6, 2013), 1844-1846.
51. *The Health Consequences of Involuntary Exposure to Tobacco Smoke: A Report of the Surgeon General*, (Atlanta: U.S. Department of Health and Human Services, 2006), 11.
52. Quoted in John O'Neil, "Surgeon General Warns of Secondhand Smoke," *The New York Times*, June 27, 2006, https://www.nytimes.com/2006/06/27/health/27cnd-smoke.html

53. National Center for Statistics and Analysis, *2017 Fatal Motor Vehicle Crashes: Overview*, (Washington, DC: National Highway Traffic Safety Administration, October 2018).

54. Stephen T. Ziliak and Deirdre N. McCloskey, *The Cult of Statistical Significance*, (Ann Arbor: The University of Michigan Press, 2008), 5.

55. Ziliak and McCloskey, *The Cult of Statistical Significance*, 15.

56. Stanton A. Glantz, "Smokefree Laws Cut Heart Attacks (And Other Bad Things): Look at All the Evidence," University of California San Francisco Center for Tobacco Control Research and Education, February 15, 2017, https://tobacco.ucsf.edu/smokefree-laws-cut-heart-attacks-and-other-bad-things-look-all-evidence.

57. "Secondhand Smoke (SHS) Facts," Centers for Disease Control and Prevention, accessed May 20, 2019, https://www.cdc.gov/tobacco/data_statistics/fact_sheets/secondhand_smoke/general_facts/index.htm.

58. Mattias Oberg et al., "Worldwide Burden of Disease from Exposure to Second-hand Smoke: A Retrospective Analysis of Data from 192 Countries," *The Lancet*, 377, no. 9760 (January 8, 2011), 139-146.

59. Brian Rostron, "Mortality Risks Associated with Environmental Tobacco Smoke Exposure in the United States," *Nicotine and Tobacco Research*, 15, no. 10 (October 2013), 1722-1728.

60. Brian Rostron, "Smoking-Attributable Mortality by Cause in the United States: Revising the CDC's Data and Estimates," *Nicotine and Tobacco Research*, 15, no. 1 (January 2013), 238-246.

61. American Nonsmokers' Rights Foundation, "Overview List – Number of Smokefree and Other Tobacco-Related Laws," last modified July 1, 2019.

62. Rostron, "Mortality Risks Associated with Environmental Tobacco Smoke Exposure in the United States."

63. Lawrence K. Altman, "The Evidence Mounts on Passive Smoking," *The New York Times*, May 29, 1990, https://www.nytimes.com/1990/05/29/science/the-evidence-mounts-on-passive-smoking.html.

64. Quoted in Roni Caryn Rabin, "A New Cigarette Hazard: 'Third-Hand Smoke," *The New York Times*, January 2, 2009, https://www.nytimes.com/2009/01/03/health/research/03smoke.html.

65. Quoted in Coco Ballantyne, "What is Third-Hand Smoke? Is it Hazardous?," *Scientific American*, January 6, 2009, https://www.scientificamerican.com/article/what-is-third-hand-smoke/.

66. LA BioMed, "LA BioMed Study Finds 'Thirdhand Smoke' Poses Danger to Unborn Babies' Lungs," press release, April 19, 2011, https://www.eurekalert.org/pub_releases/2011-04/labr-lbs041911.php.

67. Virender K. Rehan, Reiko Sakurai, and John S. Torday, "Thirdhand Smoke: A New Dimension to the Effects of Cigarette Smoke on the

Developing Lung," *American Journal of Physiology*, 301, no. 1 (July 2011), L1-L8.

68. Mike Pearl, "Third-Hand Smoke Could Kill You," *Vice*, February 4, 2014, https://www.vice.com/en_us/article/jmbpq7/thirdhand-smoke-could-kill-you.

69. Quoted in Susan Brink, "Thirdhand Smoke is Real – And Risky to Your Health," *National Geographic*, March 20, 2014, https://news.nationalgeographic.com/news/2014/03/140320-thirdhand-smoke-cigarettes-cancer/.

70. Peyton Jacob, III et al., "Thirdhand Smoke: New Evidence, Challenges, and Future Directions," *Chemical Research in Toxicology*, 30, no. 1, (November 30, 2016), 270-294.

71. Tobacco-Related Disease Research Program, "Grant List," accessed August 15, 2019, http://trdrp.yes4yes.com/fundedresearch/grant_list.php.

72. Miriam Stoppard, "Third-Hand Smoke is a Silent Killer that Can Be Absorbed Through the Skin," *The Daily Mirror*, October 26, 2017, https://www.mirror.co.uk/lifestyle/health/third-hand-smoke-silent-killer-11415024.

73. Quoted in Rabin, "A New Cigarette Hazard: 'Third-Hand Smoke.'"

74. Quoted in Lynne Peeples, "Your nose knows: The invisible threat of 'thirdhand smoke,'" *The Huffington Post*, August 26, 2011, https://www.huffpost.com/entry/thirdhand-smoke-smoking-risks_n_938241.

75. Simone Dennis, *Smokefree*, (London: Bloomsbury Academic, 2016), 140-141.

76. Dennis, *Smokefree*, 142.

77. Michael Siegel, email to author, June 12, 2013.

78. Michael Siegel, email to author, June 12, 2013.

79. Geoffrey C. Kabat, *Hyping Health Risks*, (New York: Columbia University Press, 2008), 176.

80. John P. A. Ioannidis, "Why Most Published Research Findings Are False," *PLoS Medicine*, 2, no. 8 (August 30, 2005), e124.

81. Energy Policy Institute at the University of Chicago, "Pollution Facts," accessed July 22, 2019, https://aqli.epic.uchicago.edu/pollution-facts/.

5. ROOMS OF THEIR OWN

1. Richard Klein, *Cigarettes Are Sublime*, (Durham: Duke University Press, 1993), 15.

2. Parts of this chapter are adapted from Jacob Grier, "Banning Smoking in

Oregon," *America's Future Foundation*, January 19, 2009, https://americasfuture.org/banning-smoking-in-oregon/.

3. Brian Libby, "Brass Tacks," *Imbibe*, July/August 2006, 28-31.
4. Jacob Grier, "Let's Not Pretend It's About Saving Lives," *The Oregonian*, December 29, 2008, https://www.oregonlive.com/opinion/2008/12/lets_not_pretend_its_about_sav.html.
5. Amy J. Ruiz, "Smoke 'Em While You've Got 'Em," *The Portland Mercury*, December 18, 2008, https://www.portlandmercury.com/portland/smoke-em-while-youve-got-em/Content?oid=998525.
6. Ezra Johnson-Greenough, "The Don of Oregon Beer," *The New School*, January 31, 2011, https://www.newschoolbeer.com/2011/01/the-don-of-oregon-beer.html.
7. Ezra Johnson-Greenough, "An Oral History of the Horse Brass," *Willamette Week*, February 28, 2007, https://www.wweek.com/bars/beer/2017/02/28/an-oral-history-of-the-horse-brass/.
8. Peter Rowe, "Coronado Enacts Ban on Outdoor Smoking," *The San Diego Union-Tribune*, December 24, 2013, https://www.sandiegouniontribune.com/lifestyle/people/sdut-coronado-smoking-no-no-2013dec24-story.html.
9. "Overview List – Number of Smokefree and Other Tobacco-Related Laws," American Nonsmokers' Rights Foundation, last modified July 1, 2019, https://no-smoke.org/wp-content/uploads/pdf/mediaordlist.pdf.
10. "Municipalities with Smokefree Beach laws," American Nonsmokers' Rights Foundation, last modified October 2, 2017, https://no-smoke.org/wp-content/uploads/pdf/SmokefreeBeaches.pdf.
11. "Municipalities with Smokefree Park Laws," American Nonsmokers' Rights Foundation, last modified October 2, 2017, https://no-smoke.org/wp-content/uploads/pdf/SmokefreeParks.pdf.
12. "Municipalities with Smokefree Outdoor Dining and Bar Patio Laws," American Nonsmokers' Rights Foundation, last modified April 1, 2019, https://no-smoke.org/wp-content/uploads/pdf/SmokefreeOutdoorDining.pdf.
13. "Overview List – Number of Smokefree and Other Tobacco-Related Laws," American Nonsmokers' Rights Foundation, last modified July 1, 2019, https://no-smoke.org/wp-content/uploads/pdf/mediaordlist.pdf.
14. Cited in Simon Chapman, "Banning Smoking Outdoors Is Seldom Ethically Justifiable," *Tobacco Control*, 9, no. 1, 97.
15. Stanton A. Glantz, "Achieving a Smokefree Society," *Circulation*, 76, no. 4 (October 1987), 747.
16. Quoted in Sewell Chan, "New York Eyes 'No Smoking' Outdoors, Too," *The New York Times*, September 14, 2009, https://www.nytimes.com/2009/09/15/nyregion/15smoking.html.

17. Cited in Ronald Bayer and Kathleen E. Bachynski, "Banning Smoking in Parks and on Beaches: Science, Policy, and the Politics of Denormalization," *Public Health*, 32, no. 7 (2013), 1296.

18. Robert H. Bork, *The Tempting of America*, (New York: Touchstone, 1990), 123.

19. Kirsten Bell et al., "'Every Space Is Claimed': Smokers' Experiences of Tobacco Denormalization," *Sociology of Health & Illness*, 32, no. 6 (September 2010), 914-929.

20. Centers for Disease Control and Prevention, "Current Cigarette Smoking Among Adults in the United States," accessed May 15, 2019, https://www.cdc.gov/tobacco/data_statistics/fact_sheets/adult_data/cig_smoking/index.htm.

21. Quoted in Heidi Groover, "The ACLU and the Low Income Housing Institute Are Opposed to the Proposed Smoking Ban in Parks," *The Stranger*, May 8, 2015, https://www.thestranger.com/blogs/slog/2015/05/08/22185464/the-aclu-and-the-low-income-housing-institute-are-opposed-to-the-proposed-smoking-ban-in-parks.

22. Christian Hill, "City May Ban Dogs, Smoking Downtown," *The Register-Guard*, February 9, 2017, https://www.registerguard.com/rg/news/local/35262355-75/eugene-council-mulls-bans-on-dogs-smoking-downtown.html.csp.

23. Joseph R. Paolino, "Make Downtown Providence Smoke-Free," *Providence Journal*, June 24, 2015, https://www.providencejournal.com/article/20150624/OPINION/150629695.

24. June Thunderstorm, "Off Our Butts," *The Baffler*, December 2016, https://thebaffler.com/salvos/off-our-butts-thunderstorm.

25. Simone Dennis, *Smokefree*, (London: Bloomsbury Academic, 2016), 66.

26. "Governor Mitt Romney Signs Massachusetts Smoking Ban (Mitt Romney Archive, 2004)," *The Republican*, May 20, 2012, https://www.masslive.com/mitt-romney-archive/2012/05/mitt_romney_signs_smoking_ban.html.

27. Jeffrey Young, "Huckabee About-Face on Smoking," *The Hill*, January 16, 2008, https://thehill.com/homenews/news/14052-huckabee-about-face-on-smoking.

28. Palko Karasz, "Austria's Far Right Wants the Freedom to Smoke," *The New York Times*, March 18, 2018, https://www.nytimes.com/2018/03/18/world/europe/austria-smoking-ban.html.

29. Barbara Ehrenreich, "Barbara Ehrenreich Doesn't Have Time for Self-Care," interview by Isaac Chotiner, *Slate*, April 13, 2018, https://slate.com/news-and-politics/2018/04/barbara-ehrenreich-says-smoking-bans-are-a-war-on-the-working-class.html.

30. Laura Dimon and Erin Durkin, "Councilman's Bill Would Ban Smoking

While Walking on City Sidewalks," *New York Daily News*, March 20, 2018, https://www.nydailynews.com/new-york/councilman-bill-ban-smoking-walking-sidewalks-article-1.3886435.

31. Oregon Health Authority, "Smoke Shop and Cigar Bar Certification," accessed May 18, 2019, https://www.oregon.gov/oha/PH/PREVENTIONWELLNESS/TOBACCOPREVENTION/SMOKEFREEWORKPLACELAW/Pages/certification.aspx.

32. Thomas A. Garrett and Michael R. Pakko, "The Revenue Performance of Casinos After a Smoking Ban: The Case of Illinois," working paper, Federal Reserve Bank of St. Louis Research Division, March, 2010.

33. Quoted in Andrew Nagy, "D.C. Council Legalize Cigar-Smoking Events," *Cigar Aficionado*, March 5, 2010, https://www.cigaraficionado.com/article/dc-council-legalizes-cigar-smoking-events-3824.

34. Mike DeBonis, "D.C. Council Set to Narrow Smoking Ban Exemption," *The Washington Post*, June 8, 2011, https://www.washingtonpost.com/blogs/mike-debonis/post/dc-council-set-to-narrow-smoking-ban-exemption/2011/07/08/gIQA9UYF4H_blog.html?utm_term=.dac9e94f7652&wprss=mike-debonis.

35. Quoted in Peter Rowe, "Coronado Enacts Ban on Outdoor Smoking," *The San Diego Union-Tribune*, December 24, 2013.

36. Quoted in Seth Wright, "Ban Threatens Hookah," *The Daily Tar Heel*, May 20, 2009, https://www.dailytarheel.com/article/2009/05/ban-threatens-hookahbr.

37. Megan McArdle, "'Ban Smoking' Means 'Evict Defiant Smokers,'" *Bloomberg*, November 12, 2015, https://www.bloomberg.com/opinion/articles/2015-11-12/-ban-smoking-means-evict-defiant-smokers-.

38. German Lopez, "The Case for Banning Smoking Indoors – Even in Your Home," *Vox*, November 12, 2015, https://www.vox.com/policy-and-politics/2015/11/12/9725176/smoking-bans-public-housing.

39. Dylan Matthews, "Banning Smoking in Public Housing Singles Out the Poor. But It Also Saves Lives," *Vox*, November 15, 2015, https://www.vox.com/policy-and-politics/2015/11/15/9732162/public-housing-smoking-ban.

40. John Stuart Mill, *On Liberty and Other Writings*, ed. Stefan Collini (Cambridge: Cambridge University Press, 1989), 13.

41. Naomi Oreskes and Erik M. Conway, *Merchants of Doubt*, (New York: Bloomsbury Press, 2010), 161.

42. Jacob Grier, "Smoking Bans and Libertarian Failure," *Liquidity Preference*, June 15, 2009, http://www.jacobgrier.com/blog/archives/2317.html.

43. Margie Skeer et al., "Town-Level Characteristics and Smoking Policy Adoption in Massachusetts: Are Local Restaurant Smoking Regulations

Fostering Disparities in Health Protection?" *American Journal of Public Health*, 94, no. 2 (February 2004), 286-292.

44. Laura Cornelsen et al., "Systematic Review and Meta-Analysis of the Economic Impact of Smoking Bans in Restaurants and Bars," *Addiction*, 109, no. 5 (February 16, 2014), 720-727.

45. Michael B. Sauter and Charles Stockdale, "The Most Dangerous Jobs in the US Include Electricians, Firefighters, and Police," *USA Today*, January 8, 2019, https://www.usatoday.com/story/money/2019/01/08/most-dangerous-jobs-us-where-fatal-injuries-happen-most-often/38832907/.

46. Jill Janocha, "Facts of the Catch: Occupation Injuries, Illnesses, and Fatalities to Fishing Workers, 2003-2009," *Beyond the Numbers*, August 2012, https://www.bls.gov/opub/btn/volume-1/facts-of-the-catch-occupational-injuries-illnesses-and-fatalities-to-fishing-workers-2003-2009.htm.

47. J. Lincoln, "Commercial Fishing Deaths – United States, 2000-2009," *Morbidity and Mortality Weekly Report*, July 16, 2010, https://www.cdc.gov/mmwr/preview/mmwrhtml/mm5927a2.htm.

48. James Poulos, "Welcome to the Pink Police State: Regime Change in America," *The Federalist*, July 17, 2014, https://thefederalist.com/2014/07/17/welcome-to-the-pink-police-state-regime-change-in-america/.

49. James Poulos, "The New Social Divide Within the Pink Police State," *The Federalist*, July 23, 2014, https://thefederalist.com/2014/07/23/the-new-social-divide-within-the-pink-police-state/.

50. Simon Chapman, "Banning Smoking Outdoors Is Seldom Ethically Justifiable," *Tobacco Control*, 9, no. 1, 95.

51. Michael Siegel, "Going Too Far: POST #2 – Complete College Smoking Bans," *The Rest of the Story*, April 9, 2007, http://tobaccoanalysis.blogspot.com/2007/04/going-too-far-post-2-complete-college.html.

52. Michael Siegel, "On Car Smoking Bans and Class Discrimination," *The Rest of the Story*, April 10, 2007, http://tobaccoanalysis.blogspot.com/2007/04/on-car-smoking-bans-and-class.html.

53. C. R. Roberts, "Tacoma Tries to Douse Cigar Smoking Lounge," *The Seattle Times*, March 24, 2010, https://www.seattletimes.com/seattle-news/tacoma-tries-to-douse-cigar-smoking-lounge/.

54. Paul Farrell, "Smokers Win Out Over Diners at Some NSW Pubs and Bars: Health Groups," *The Guardian*, December 24, 2015, https://www.theguardian.com/society/2015/dec/25/smokers-win-out-over-outside-diners-at-some-nsw-pubs-and-bars-health-groups.

55. Quoted in Serita Braxton, "Smokers on the Spree," *Exberliner*, March 7, 2017, http://www.exberliner.com/features/zeitgeist/smokers-on-the-spree/.

6. BOOTLEGGERS AND BAPTISTS

1. Deirdre N. McCloskey, *Bourgeois Equality*, (Chicago: The University of Chicago Press, 2016), 619.
2. Barack Obama, "Remarks on Signing the Family Smoking Prevention and Tobacco Control Act of 2009," *Public Papers of the Presidents of the United States: Barack Obama, 2009, Book 1*, (Washington, DC: Government Printing Office, 2011), 872.
3. Timothy P. Carney, *Obamanomics*, (Washington: Regnery Publishing, 2009), 173-177.
4. *Roll Call* Staff, "How Philip Morris, Tobacco Foes Tied the Knot," *Roll Call*, October 4, 2004, https://www.rollcall.com/news/-7035-1.html.
5. Joe Nocera, "Unlikely Partners in a Cause," *The New York Times*, June 19, 2009, https://www.nytimes.com/2009/06/20/business/20nocera.html?_r=1.
6. Adam Smith, *An Inquiry into the Nature and Causes of the Wealth of Nations, Volume I*, ed. R. H. Campbell and A. S. Skinner, (Indianapolis: Liberty Fund, 1981), 267.
7. Bruce Yandle, "Bootleggers and Baptists – The Education of a Regulatory Economist," *AEI Journal of Government and Society*, May/June 1983, 12-16.
8. Adam Smith and Bruce Yandle, *Bootleggers and Baptists*, (Washington, DC: Cato Institute, 2014), 3.
9. Yandle, "Bootleggers and Baptists – The Education of a Regulatory Economist," 13.
10. Allan M. Brandt, *The Cigarette Century*, (New York: Basic Books, 2007), 404-405.
11. Martha A. Derthick, *Up in Smoke*, (Washington, DC: CQ Press, 2012), 29-35.
12. Viscusi, *Smoke-Filled Rooms*, 16.
13. Viscusi, *Smoke-Filled Rooms*, 93-99.
14. Derthick, *Up in Smoke*, 166-171.
15. Derthick, *Up in Smoke*, 84-89.
16. Viscusi, *Smoke-Filled Rooms*, 17-24.
17. Viscusi, *Smoke-Filled Rooms*, 25.
18. Viscusi, *Smoke-Filled Rooms*, 26-32.
19. Viscusi, *Smoke-Filled Rooms*, 37-42.
20. Derthick, *Up in Smoke*, 190.
21. Viscusi, *Smoke-Filled Rooms*, 34-37.
22. Viscusi, *Smoke-Filled Rooms*, 40.
23. Alison Snow Jones et al., "Funding of North Carolina Tobacco Control

Programs Through the Master Settlement Agreement," *American Journal of Public Health*, 97, no. 1, (January 2007), 36-44.

24. Walter J. Jones and Gerard A. Silvestri, "The Master Settlement Agreement and Its Impact on Tobacco Use 10 Years Later," *Chest*, 137, no. 3 (March 2010), 692-700.

25. Walter K. Olson, *The Rule of Lawyers*, (New York: Truman Talley Books, 2003), 47-69.

26. Viscusi, *Smoke-Filled Rooms*, 54.

27. Olson, *The Rule of Lawyers*, 64.

28. Jones and Silvestri, "The Master Settlement Agreement and Its Impact on Tobacco Use 10 Years Later," 695.

29. Smith and Yandle, *Bootleggers and Baptists*, 98.

30. Quoted in Myron Levin, "States' Tobacco Settlement Has Failed to Clear the Air," *The Los Angeles Times*, November 9, 2003, https://www.latimes.com/archives/la-xpm-2003-nov-09-fi-smoke9-story.html.

31. Quoted in Thomas Farragher, "Little of $246b Deal Fights Tobacco," *The Boston Globe*, August 9, 2001.

32. Parts of this chapter are adapted from Jacob Grier, "How the FDA Is Keeping New Cigarettes Off the Market," *The Atlantic*, March 6, 2013, https://www.theatlantic.com/health/archive/2013/03/how-the-fda-is-keeping-new-cigarettes-off-the-market/273679/. © 2013 Jacob Grier, as first published on TheAtlantic.com.

33. *Family Smoking Prevention and Tobacco Control Act*, Public Law 111-131, *U.S. Statutes at Large* 123 (2009) 1776-1852.

34. Quoted in Samuel Loewenberg, "Smoke Screen," *Slate*, July 25, 2002, https://slate.com/business/2002/07/why-does-philip-morris-want-the-fda-to-regulate-cigarettes.html.

35. P. A. McDaniel and R. E. Malone, "Understanding Philip Morris's Pursuit of US Government Regulation of Tobacco," *Tobacco Control*, 14, no. 3, (2005), 193-200.

36. Jacob Sullum, "Bad Taste," *Reason*, May 28, 2004, https://reason.com/2004/05/28/bad-taste-2.

37. Michael Felberbaum, "FDA Review of Tobacco Products Grinds to a Halt," Associated Press, December 13, 2012.

38. Toni Clarke, "U.S. Approves Two New Newport Cigarettes in First Use of New Powers," Reuters, June 25, 2003.

39. Quoted in Catherine Saint Louis, "F.D.A. Orders 4 Bidi Cigarette Brands Removed from Shelves," *The New York Times*, February 21, 2014, https://www.nytimes.com/2014/02/22/us/fda-orders-4-bidi-cigarette-brands-removed-from-shelves.html.

40. Michael Felberbaum, "FDA Tells Company to Stop Sale of Tobacco Products," Associated Press, February 21, 2014.

41. United States Food and Drug Administration, "Tobacco Product Marketing Orders," accessed May 25, 2019, https://www.fda.gov/tobacco-products/market-and-distribute-tobacco-product/tobacco-product-marketing-orders.

42. Grier, "How the FDA is Keeping New Cigarettes Off the Market," *The Atlantic*.

43. United States Food and Drug Administration, "Statement of Andrew C. von Eschenbach, Commissioner of Food and Drugs, before the Subcommittee on Health, House Committee on Energy and Commerce," October 3, 2007.

44. Micah Berman, "The Faltering Promise of FDA Tobacco Regulation," *Saint Louis Journal of Health Law and Policy*, 12, (June 10, 2019), 145-167.

45. United States Food and Drug Administration, "Deeming Tobacco Products to Be Subject to the Food, Drug, and Cosmetic Act, as Amended by the Family Smoking Prevention and Tobacco Control Act; Regulations Restricting the Sale and Distribution of Tobacco Products and Required Warning Statements for Tobacco Product Packages and Advertisements," May 2016, https://www.fda.gov/media/97875/download.

46. United States Food and Drug Administration, "Deeming Tobacco Products to Be Subject to the Food, Drug, and Cosmetic Act, as Amended by the Family Smoking Prevention and Tobacco Control Act; Regulations Restricting the Sale and Distribution of Tobacco Products and Required Warning Statements for Tobacco Product Packages and Advertisements, Final Regulatory Impact Analysis," 27-28.

47. United States Food and Drug Administration, "Deeming Tobacco Products to Be Subject to the Food, Drug, and Cosmetic Act, as Amended by the Family Smoking Prevention and Tobacco Control Act; Regulations Restricting the Sale and Distribution of Tobacco Products and Required Warning Statements for Tobacco Product Packages and Advertisements, Final Regulatory Impact Analysis" 93-98.

48. United States Food and Drug Administration, "Deeming Tobacco Products to Be Subject to the Food, Drug, and Cosmetic Act, as Amended by the Family Smoking Prevention and Tobacco Control Act; Regulations Restricting the Sale and Distribution of Tobacco Products and Required Warning Statements for Tobacco Product Packages and Advertisements, Final Regulatory Impact Analysis," 75-78.

49. United States Food and Drug Administration, "Deeming Tobacco Products to Be Subject to the Food, Drug, and Cosmetic Act, as Amended by the Family Smoking Prevention and Tobacco Control Act; Regulations Restricting the Sale and Distribution of Tobacco Products and Required Warning Statements for Tobacco Product Packages and Advertisements, Final Regulatory Analysis," 103.

50. Parts of this chapter are adapted from Jacob Grier, "Scott Gottlieb's FDA Is Moving Toward a Stealth Ban on Cigarettes and Cigars," *Reason*, November 26, 2018, https://reason.com/2018/11/26/gottlieb-fda-vape-cigar-cigarette-ban/.

51. United States Food and Drug Administration, "FDA Announces Comprehensive Regulatory Plan to Shift Trajectory of Tobacco-Related Disease," July 28, 2017, https://www.fda.gov/news-events/press-announcements/fda-announces-comprehensive-regulatory-plan-shift-trajectory-tobacco-related-disease-death.

52. Action on Smoking and Health et al., "Joint Letter to the FDA on a Nicotine Standard Proposed Rule," July 16, 2018, https://www.aafp.org/dam/AAFP/documents/advocacy/prevention/tobacco/LT-FDA-NicotineStandardProposedRule-071618.pdf.

53. United States Food and Drug Administration, "Deeming Tobacco Products to Be Subject to the Food, Drug, and Cosmetic Act, as Amended by the Family Smoking Prevention and Tobacco Control Act; Regulations Restricting the Sale and Distribution of Tobacco Products and Required Warning Statements for Tobacco Product Packages and Advertisements, Final Regulatory Impact Analysis" 60-61.

54. Clive Bates and Carrie Wade, "Reducing Nicotine in Cigarettes: Challenges and Opportunities," R Street Policy Study No. 115, October 2017, http://www.rstreet.org/wp-content/uploads/2017/10/115.pdf.

55. Action on Smoking and Health et al., "Joint Letter to the FDA on a Nicotine Standard Proposed Rule."

56. Eric C. Donny and Melissa Jones, "Prolonged Exposure to Denicotinized Cigarettes With or Without Transdermal Nicotine," *Drug and Alcohol Dependence*, 104, no. 1-2 (September 2009), 23-33.

57. United States Food and Drug Administration, ""Deeming Tobacco Products to Be Subject to the Food, Drug, and Cosmetic Act, as Amended by the Family Smoking Prevention and Tobacco Control Act; Regulations on the Sale and Distribution of Tobacco Products and Required Warning Statements for Tobacco Products," April 25, 2014, https://www.govinfo.gov/content/pkg/FR-2014-04-25/pdf/2014-09491.pdf.

58. Andrew Nagy, "House Bill Would Block Regulation of Premium Cigars," *Cigar Aficionado*, March 26, 2019, https://www.cigaraficionado.com/article/house-bill-would-block-regulation-of-premium-cigars.

7. NON-BURNING ISSUES

1. Peter McWilliams, *Ain't Nobody's Business if You Do*, (Allen Park, Michigan: MaryBooks, 1996), 256-257.
2. Parts of this chapter are adapted from Jacob Grier, "We Are Completely Overreacting to Vaping," *Slate*, January 29, 2019, https://slate.com/technology/2019/01/vaping-is-good-anti-smoker-bias.html.
3. The Real Cost, "Vaping Is an Epidemic," YouTube video, 0:30, September 17, 2018, https://youtu.be/zYuyS1Oq8gY.
4. NYU College of Global Public Health, "E-Cigarettes: The Tectonic Shift in Nicotine and Tobacco Consumption [Part 1]," YouTube video, 1:36:14, December 18, 2018, https://youtu.be/Im7JnAKEkrU.
5. Quoted in Tim Craig, "Should E-Cigarettes Be Banned Indoors in D.C.?" *The Washington Post*, April 9, 2013.
6. Board of Health for Multnomah County, "Order No. 2015-011," February 12, 2015, https://multco.us/file/38547/download.
7. Quoted in Vanessa Ho, "King County Bans E-Cigarette Smoking," *Seattle Post-Intelligencer*, December 15, 2010, https://www.seattlepi.com/local/article/King-County-bans-public-e-cigarette-smoking-904130.php.
8. Quoted in Reuters, "France to Ban Electronic Cigarettes in Public," Reuters, May 31, 2013, https://in.reuters.com/article/france-cigarettes/france-to-ban-electronic-cigarettes-in-public-idINDEE94U0AH20130531.
9. Lars Ramström, Ron Borland, and Tom Wikmans, "Patterns of Snus Use in Sweden: Implications for Public Health," *International Journal of Environmental Research and Public Health*, 13, no. 11, (November 9, 2016), 1110.
10. Statistics Norway, "Snus More Used than Cigarettes," January 18, 2018, https://www.ssb.no/en/helse/artikler-og-publikasjoner/snus-more-used-than-cigarettes.
11. Statistics Norway, "Snus More Used than Cigarettes."
12. Thor S, Editor, "Skolelevers drogvanor (Alcohol and Drug Use Among Students)," Centralförbundet för alkohol- och narkotikaupplysning, CAN (Swedish Council for Information on Alcohol and Other Drugs, CAN), Rapport 170, 2017. Swedish.
13. Eurostat, "Tobacco Consumption Statistics," accessed May 26, 2019, https://ec.europa.eu/eurostat/statistics-explained/index.php/Tobacco_consumption_statistics#Daily_smokers_of_cigarettes.
14. Eurostat, "File: Causes of Death – Malignant Neoplasms of Trachea, Bronchus and Lung, Residents, 2014 HLTH17.png," accessed May 26, 2019, https://ec.europa.eu/eurostat/statistics-explained/index.php?title=File:Causes_of_death_%E2%80%90

94_malignant_neoplasms_of_trachea,_bronchus_and_lung,_residents,_2 014_HLTH17.png.

15. Lars Ramström and Tom Wikmans, "Mortality Attributable to Tobacco Among Men in Sweden and Other European Countries: An Analysis of Data in a WHO Report," *Tobacco Induced Diseases*, 12, no. 14, 2014.

16. Karl Erik Lund and Tord Finne Vedoy, "Relative Risk Perceptions Between Snus and Cigarettes in a Snus-Prevalent Society – An Observational Study Over a 16 year Period," *International Journal of Environmental Research and Public Health*, 16, no. 5, (March 2019), 879.

17. Lars E. Rutqvist et al., "Swedish Snus and the GothiaTek Standard," *Harm Reduction Journal*, 8, no. 11, May 16, 2011.

18. Smita Asthana et al., "Association of Oral Tobacco Use and Oral Cancer: A Systematic Global Review and Meta-Analysis," *Nicotine and Tobacco Research*, (May 2018).

19. Peter Lee and Jan Hamling, "Systematic Review of the Relation Between Smokeless Tobacco and Cancer in Europe and North America," *BMC Health*, 7, no. 36, (July 2009).

20. Paolo Boffetta et al., "Smokeless Tobacco and Cancer," *The Lancet*, 9, no. 7, (July 2008), 667-75.

21. Jenny Hansson et al., "Use of Snus and Acute Myocardial Infarction: Pooled Analysis of Eight Prospective Observational Studies," *European Journal of Epidemiology*, 27, no. 10, (October 2012), 771-779.

22. Brian L. Rostron et al., "Smokeless Tobacco Use and Circulatory Disease Risk: A Systematic Review and Meta-Analysis," *Open Heart*, 5, no. 2 (2018), e000846.

23. David T. Levy et al., "The Relative Risks of a Low-Nitrosamine Smokeless Tobacco Product Compared with Smoking Cigarettes," *Cancer Epidemiology, Biomarkers, & Prevention*, 13, no. 12, (December 2004), 2035-2042.

24. Ramström et al., "Patterns of Snus Use in Sweden: Implications for Public Health."

25. Ramström et al., "Patterns of Snus Use in Sweden: Implications for Public Health."

26. Karl Erik Lund, Ann McNeil, and Janne Scheffels, "The Use of Snus for Quitting Compared with Medicinal Products," *Nicotine and Tobacco Research*, 12, no. 8, (August 2010), 817-822.

27. Ramström et al., "Patterns of Snus Use in Sweden: Implications for Public Health."

28. Christopher Snowdon, *The Art of Suppression*, (Ripon, North Yorkshire: Little Dice, 2011), 149-151.

29. Eric Boehm, "Incoming FDA Commissioner Sharpless Shouldn't Stop Snus, the Safer Swedish Smoking Alternative," *Reason*, April 3, 2019,

https://reason.com/2019/04/03/fda-commissioner-shouldnt-stop-snus/.

30. Todd C. Frankel, "Meet the Cancer Doctor Who Wants the FDA to Soften Tobacco Warnings," *The Washington Post*, April 8, 2015, https://www.washingtonpost.com/news/wonk/wp/2015/04/08/meet-the-cancer-doctor-who-wants-the-fda-to-soften-tobacco-warnings/

31. Michael Russell, "Low-Tar Medium-Nicotine Cigarettes: A New Approach to Safer Smoking," *British Medical Journal*, 1, no. 6023 (June 1976), 1430-1433.

32. Richard Kluger, *Ashes to Ashes*, (New York: Alfred A Knopf, 1996), 603-604.

33. Nancy Amodei and Rick Lamb, "Over-the-Counter Nicotine Replacement Therapy: Can Its Impact on Smoking Cessation Be Enhanced?" *Psychology of Addictive Behaviors*, 22, no. 4, (December 2008), 472-485.

34. Julian Morris and Amir Ullan Khan, "The Vapor Revolution," Reason Foundation Working Paper, August, 2016, 1-4, https://reason.org/wp-content/uploads/2016/08/vapour_revolution_working_paper.pdf.

35. Morris and Khan, "The Vapor Revolution," 9-13.

36. Amelia Howard, PhD candidate, University of Waterloo, email to author, August 14, 2019.

37. Morris and Khan, "The Vapor Revolution," 14.

38. David Pierce, "This Might Just Be the First Great E-Cig," *Wired*, April 21, 2015, https://www.wired.com/2015/04/pax-juul-ecig/.

39. Olivia Zaleski, "E-Cigarette Maker Juul Labs Is Raising $1.2 Billion," *Bloomberg*, June 29, 2018, https://www.bloomberg.com/news/articles/2018-06-29/e-cigarette-maker-juul-labs-is-raising-1-2-billion.

40. Laurel Wamsley, "Altria Buys 35 Percent Stake in E-Cigarette Maker Juul," December 20, 2018, https://www.npr.org/2018/12/20/678915071/altria-buys-35-percent-stake-in-e-cigarette-maker-juul.

41. Philip Morris International, "Our Tobacco Heating System," accessed May 28, 2019, https://www.pmi.com/smoke-free-products/iqos-our-tobacco-heating-system.

42. United States Food and Drug Administration, "FDA Permits Sale of IQOS Tobacco Heating System Through Premarket Tobacco Product Application Pathway," April 30, 2019, https://www.fda.gov/news-events/press-announcements/fda-permits-sale-iqos-tobacco-heating-system-through-premarket-tobacco-product-application-pathway.

43. Duff Wilson, "Judge Orders F.D.A. to Stop Blocking Imports of E-Cigarettes from China," *The New York Times*, January 14, 2010, https://www.nytimes.com/2010/01/15/business/15smoke.html.

44. Parts of this chapter are adapted from Jacob Grier, "The FDA Is Scrapping the Obama-Era Approach to E-Cig Regulation. Good," *Slate*, August

1, 2017, https://slate.com/technology/2017/08/the-fdas-new-approach-to-cigarettes-is-good-for-public-health.html.

45. United States Food and Drug Administration, "Deeming Tobacco Products to Be Subject to the Food, Drug, and Cosmetic Act, as Amended by the Family Smoking Prevention and Tobacco Control Act; Regulations Restricting the Sale and Distribution of Tobacco Products and Required Warning Statements for Tobacco Product Packages and Advertisements, Final Regulatory Impact Analysis," May 2016, 88-90, https://www.fda.gov/media/97875/download.

46. United States Food and Drug Administration, "Deeming Tobacco Products to Be Subject to the Food, Drug, and Cosmetic Act, as Amended by the Family Smoking Prevention and Tobacco Control Act; Regulations Restricting the Sale and Distribution of Tobacco Products and Required Warning Statements for Tobacco Product Packages and Advertisements," 94.

47. United States Food and Drug Administration, "Deeming Tobacco Products to Be Subject to the Food, Drug, and Cosmetic Act, as Amended by the Family Smoking Prevention and Tobacco Control Act; Regulations Restricting the Sale and Distribution of Tobacco Products and Required Warning Statements for Tobacco Product Packages and Advertisements," April 2014, 35-36, https://www.fda.gov/media/88754/download.

48. Jacob Grier, "The FDA Is Scrapping the Obama-Era Approach to E-Cig Regulation. Good." *Slate*, August 1, 2017, https://slate.com/technology/2017/08/the-fdas-new-approach-to-cigarettes-is-good-for-public-health.html.

49. Uday Sampath and Chris Kirkham, "U.S. Federal Judge Orders FDA to Implement 10-Month Deadline for E-Cig Applications," Reuters, July 12, 2019.

50. United States Food and Drug Administration, "Premarket Tobacco Product Applications for Electronic Nicotine Delivery Systems," June 2019, https://www.fda.gov/media/127853/download.

51. Jim McDonald, 'Pushed by Federal Court, FDA Releases PMTA Guidance," June 17, 2019, *Vaping360*, https://vaping360.com/vape-news/80820/aap-lawsuit-forces-fda-to-release-pmta-guidance/.

52. Jacob Sullum, "The FDA's Plan to Ban Flavored E-Cigarettes from Most Stores Is Unfair and Dangerous," *Reason*, November 9, 2011, https://reason.com/2018/11/09/the-fdas-plan-to-ban-flavored-e-cigarett/.

53. Catherine Ho, "Juul Escalates Fight Against E-Cigarette Bans," *San Francisco Chronicle*, July 17, 2019, https://www.sfchronicle.com/business/article/First-San-Francisco-now-Livermore-Juul-fights-14103075.php?psid=dvaFM.

54. Royal College of Physicians, *Nicotine Without Smoke*, (London: RCP,

2016), 83-84.

55. Cochrane Tobacco Addiction Review Group, written evidence submitted to UK Parliament, December 2017, http://data.parliament.uk/writtenevidence/committeeevidence.svc/evidencedocument/science-and-technology-committee/ecigarettes/written/75240.html.

56. American Cancer Society Board of Directors, "American Cancer Society Position Statement on E-Cigarettes," accessed May 29, 2019, https://www.cancer.org/healthy/stay-away-from-tobacco/e-cigarette-position-statement.html.

57. Peter Hajek et al., "A Randomized Trial of E-Cigarettes versus Nicotine-Replacement Therapy," *The New England Journal of Medicine*, 380, no. 7 (February 14, 2019), 629-637.

58. Shu-Hong Zhu et al., "E-Cigarette Use and Associated Changes in Population Smoking Cessation: Evidence from US Current Population Surveys," *British Medical Journal*, 358, no. 3262 (July 26, 2017).

59. Sarah Jackson et al., "Moderators of Real-World Effectiveness of Smoking Cessation Aids: A Population Study," *Addiction*, May 22, 2019.

60. Kaitlyn M. Berry et al., "E-Cigarette Initiation and Associated Changes in Smoking Cessation and Reduction: The Population Assessment of Tobacco and Health Study, 2013-2015," *Tobacco Control*, 28 (2019), 42-49.

61. Quoted in Jacob Grier, "Vape-22," *Slate*, September 11, 2018, https://slate.com/technology/2018/09/vaping-e-cigarette-fda-advertising-facts.html.

62. House of Commons Science and Technology Committee, "Oral Evidence: E-Cigarettes, HC 505," April 24, 2018, http://data.parliament.uk/writtenevidence/committeeevidence.svc/evidencedocument/science-and-technology-committee/ecigarettes/oral/82000.html.

63. Parts of this chapter are adapted from Jacob Grier, "The FDA's New E-Cigarette Regulations Respond to an 'Epidemic' that Doesn't Really Exist," *Slate*, November 16, 2018, https://slate.com/technology/2018/11/fda-ecigarettes-harm-reduction-public-health-vaping.html.

64. Karen A. Cullen et al., "Notes from the Field: Use of Electronic Cigarettes and Any Tobacco Product Among Middle and High School Students – United States, 2011-2018," *Morbidity and Mortality Weekly Report*, November 16, 2018.

65. Centers for Disease Control and Prevention, "Youth and Tobacco Use," accessed May 29, 2019, https://www.cdc.gov/tobacco/data_statistics/fact_sheets/youth_data/tobacco_use/index.htm.

66. Linda Bauld and Suzi Gage, "Vaping Among Young People Remains a Burning Issue Among Health Experts," *The Guardian*, January 4, 2019, https://www.theguardian.com/society/2019/jan/04/vaping-by-young-people-remains-burning-issue-health-experts.

67. Jean-Francois Etter, "Gateway Effects and Electronic Cigarettes," *Addic-*

tion, 113, no. 10, 1776-1783.

68. Centers for Disease Control and Prevention, "Current Cigarette Smoking Among Adults – United States, 2011," *Morbidity and Mortality Weekly Report*, November 9, 2012, https://www.cdc.gov/mmwr/preview/mmwrhtml/mm6144a2.htm.

69. Centers for Disease Control and Prevention, "Current Cigarette Smoking Among Adults in the United States," accessed May 29, 2019, https://www.cdc.gov/tobacco/data_statistics/fact_sheets/adult_data/cig_smoking/index.htm.

70. Brad Rodu, "CDC Data: Vaping Increased in 2018, Particularly Among Former Smokers," *Tobacco Truth*, July 6, 2019, https://rodutobaccotruth.blogspot.com/2019/07/cdc-data-vaping-increased-in-2018.html.

71. Lynn T. Kozlowski et al., "Applying the Risk/Use Equilibrium: Use Medicinal Nicotine Now for Harm Reduction," *Tobacco Control*, 10 (2001), 201-203.

72. David T. Levy et al., "Potential Deaths in USA by Replacing Cigarettes with E-Cigarettes," *Tobacco Control*, 27, no. 1, 18-25.

73. Royal College of Physicians, *Nicotine Without Smoke*, 187.

74. The Daily Dot, Twitter post, @dailydot, August 9, 2018, https://twitter.com/dailydot/status/1027698791653076993.

75. Scott Gottlieb, Twitter post, January 11, 2019, https://twitter.com/SGottliebFDA/status/1083688217344397313.

76. Parts of this chapter are adapted from Jacob Grier, "Vape-22," *Slate*, September 11, 2018, https://slate.com/technology/2018/09/vaping-e-cigarette-fda-advertising-facts.html.

77. Elizabeth A. Mumford et al., "Nicotine and E-Cigarette Beliefs and Policy Support Among US Smokers and Nonsmokers," *Tobacco Regulatory Science*, 3, no. 3 (July 2017), 293-305.

78. Rasmussen Reports, "Most Say E-Cigarettes No Healthier than Traditional Ones," August 16, 2018, http://www.rasmussenreports.com/public_content/lifestyle/general_lifestyle/august_2018/most_say_e_cigarettes_no_healthier_than_traditional_ones.

79. Jidong Huang et al., "Changing Perceptions of Harm of E-Cigarette vs Cigarette Use Among Adults in 2 National Surveys from 2012 to 2017," JAMA Network Open, March 29, 2019.

80. Frank Newport, "Young People Adopt Vaping as Their Smoking Rate Plummets," Gallup, July 26, 2018, https://news.gallup.com/poll/237818/young-people-adopt-vaping-smoking-rate-plummets.aspx.

81. Derek Yach, "The State of Smoking 2018," presentation, March 19, 2018, https://amadashboards.com/kp/eu_smokefree/Doc/2018%20State%20of%20Smoking%20Survey%20Findings%20and%20Insights.pdf.

82. Eli Lake, "My (Electronic) Cigarette Addiction," *The Daily Beast*, January 31, 2013, https://www.thedailybeast.com/my-electronic-cigarette-addiction.

83. Quoted in Allen Mask, "E-Cigarettes Not Effective Tool to Quit Smoking," WRAL, June 19, 2013, https://www.wral.com/lifestyles/healthteam/video/12570682/.

84. *New England Journal of Medicine*, Twitter post, @NEJM, January 21, 2015, https://twitter.com/NEJM/status/558026336259022848.

85. Kim Lacapria, "Vaping Causes Popcorn Lung?" *Snopes*, August 8, 2016, https://www.snopes.com/fact-check/vaping-causes-popcorn-lung/.

86. Elizabeth Fernandez, "Smoking E-Cigarettes Daily Doubles Risk of Heart Attacks," press release, University of California San Francisco, February 24, 2018, https://www.ucsf.edu/news/2018/02/409916/smoking-e-cigarettes-daily-doubles-risk-heart-attacks.

87. Quoted in Jia Tolentino, "The Promise of Vaping and the Rise of Juul," *The New Yorker*, May 7, 2018, https://www.newyorker.com/magazine/2018/05/14/the-promise-of-vaping-and-the-rise-of-juul.

88. United States Food and Drug Administration, "Statement from FDA Commissioner Scott Gottlieb, M.D., and Principal Deputy Commissioner Amy Abernathy, M.D., Ph.D., on FDA"s Ongoing Scientific Investigation of Potential Safety Issue Related to Seizures Reported Following E-Cigarette Use, Particularly in Youth and Young Adults," April 3, 2019, https://www.fda.gov/news-events/press-announcements/statement-fda-commissioner-scott-gottlieb-md-and-principal-deputy-commissioner-amy-abernethy-md-phd.

89. PBS's To the Contrary, "Risks of E-Cigarettes: Is Vaping the New Gateway Drug," YouTube video, 4:49, July 24, 2019, https://youtu.be/0AWVqusCLQM.

90. American Lung Association, "Another Gross Reason to Put Down the E-Cigarettes," June 27, 2019, https://www.lung.org/about-us/blog/2019/06/another-gross-reason.html.

91. Jacob Sullum, "Anti-Vaping Researchers Claim E-Cigarettes Cause Heart Attacks Before Smokers Try Them," *Reason*, July 19, 2019, https://reason.com/2019/07/19/anti-vaping-researchers-claim-e-cigarettes-cause-heart-attacks-before-smokers-try-them/.

92. Jeremy E. Drehmer et al., "Parental Smoking and E-Cigarette Use in Homes and Cars," *Pediatrics*, 143, no. 4 (April 2019).

93. Jonathan H. Adler, "Why FDA Regulations Limiting E-Cigarette Marketing May Cost Lives and Violate the Constitution," *The Washington Post*, December 12, 2017, https://www.washingtonpost.com/news/volokh-conspiracy/wp/2017/12/12/why-fda-regulations-

limiting-e-cigarette-marketing-may-cost-lives-and-violate-the-constitution/

94. Michael Siegel, "11 Million Lies: The Tobacco Control Movement Is Committing Public Health Malpractice by Misrepresenting the Health Effects of Vaping," *The Rest of the Story*, March 17, 2019, https://tobaccoanalysis.blogspot.com/2019/03/11-million-lies-tobacco-control.html.

95. Sarah Jakes, keynote speech at The E-Cigarette Summit, November 17, 2017, https://nnalliance.org/blog/211-sarah-jakes-keynote-speech-at-the-e-cig-summit-2018.

96. Virginia Berridge, *Demons*, (Oxford: Oxford University Press, 2013), 195.

97. Centers for Disease Control and Prevention, "Fact Sheets – Underage Drinking," accessed May 25, 2019, https://www.cdc.gov/alcohol/fact-sheets/underage-drinking.htm.

98. Hannah Hartig and A. W. Geiger, "About Six-in-Ten Americans Support Marijuana Legalization," Pew Research Center, October 8, 2018, https://www.pewresearch.org/fact-tank/2018/10/08/americans-support-marijuana-legalization/.

99. Royal College of Physicians, *Harm Reduction in Nicotine Addiction*, (London: Royal College of Physicians, 2007), 15.

100. Royal College of Physicians, *Harm Reduction in Nicotine Addiction*, 189-192.

101. United States Food and Drug Administration, "Trump Administration Combatting Epidemic of Youth Cigarette Use with Plan to Clear Market of Unauthorized, Non-Tobacco-Flavored E-Cigarette Products," September 11, 2019.

8. ENDGAME

1. Alan Moore, *Watchmen*, (New York: DC Comics, 1986-1987), #12, 27.

2. Kenneth Warner, "An Endgame for Tobacco?" *Tobacco Control*, 22 (May 2013), i3-i5.

3. Parts of this chapter are adapted from Jacob Grier, "Scott Gottlieb's FDA Is Moving Toward a Stealth Ban on Cigarettes and Cigars," *Reason*, November 26, 2018, https://reason.com/2018/11/26/gottlieb-fda-vape-cigar-cigarette-ban/.

4. Virginia Postrel, *The Future and Its Enemies*, (New York: Touchstone, 1988), 16-18.

5. Postrel, *The Future and Its Enemies*, 26.

6. Joseph A. Schumpeter, *Capitalism, Socialism, and Democracy*, third edition, (New York: HarperPerennial, 1975), 83-84.

7. Christopher Snowdon, *The Art of Suppression*, (North Yorkshire: Little Dice, 2011), 158-176.

8. Duff Wilson, "Judge Orders F.D.A. to Stop Blocking Imports of E-Cigarettes from China," *The New York Times*, January 14, 2010, https://www.nytimes.com/2010/01/15/business/15smoke.html.

9. Deborah Arnott, "There's No Single Endgame," *Tobacco Control*, 22 (May 2013), i38-i39.

10. Friedrich A. Hayek, *The Road to Serfdom*, fiftieth anniversary edition, (Chicago: The University of Chicago Press, 1994), 61-62.

11. Karl Lund, "Rendez-vous with Karl Lund," interview by Philippe Boucher, *THR Rendez-vous*, May 11, 2018, https://blogsofbainbridge. typepad.com/thr_rendezvous/2018/05/rendez-vous-with-karl-lund-.html.

12. Kirsten Bell, "Tobacco Control, Harm Reduction, and the Problem of Pleasure," *Drugs and Alcohol Today*, 13, no. 2 (June 2013), 111-118.

13. Mitch Zeller, "The Future of Nicotine Regulation: Key Questions and Challenges," *Nicotine and Tobacco Research*, 21, no. 3 (March 2019), 331-332.

14. Frank J. Chaloupka, Jonathan Gruber, and Kenneth E. Warner, "Accounting for 'Lost Pleasure' in a Cost-Benefit Analysis of Government Regulation: The Case for the Food and Drug Administration's Proposed Cigarette Labelling Regulation," *Annals of Internal Medicine*, 162, no. 1 (January 6, 2015), 64-65.

15. Robert Proctor, *Golden Holocaust*, (Berkeley: University of California Press, 2011), 521.

16. Simon Usborne, "Can Vapes Save the World from Smoking?" *Medical Xpress*, July 2, 2019, https://medicalxpress.com/news/2019-07-vapes-world.html.

17. Proctor, *Golden Holocaust*, 549.

18. Proctor, *Golden Holocaust*, 6.

19. Proctor, *Golden Holocaust*, 557.

20. Proctor, *Golden Holocaust*, 10.

21. Michael Mechanic, "'Golden Holocaust is the Book Big Tobacco Doesn't Want You to Read," *Mother Jones*, May 2012, https://www.motherjones. com/politics/2012/05/tobacco-book-golden-holocaust-robert-proctor/.

22. House of Representatives, Hawaii, "A Bill for an Act Relating to Cigarettes," H.B No. 1509, thirtieth legislature, 2019, https://www.capitol. hawaii.gov/session2019/bills/HB1509_.pdf.

23. K. Michael Cummings and Robert N. Proctor, "The Changing Public Image of Smoking in the United States: 1964-2014," *Cancer Epidemiology, Biomarkers and Prevention*, 23, no. 1 (January 2014), 32-36.

24. Cassandra Tate, *Cigarette Wars*, (Oxford: Oxford University Press,

1999), 62.

25. Koop, C. Everett, "Toward a Smoke-Free Society by the Year 2000," presentation to the Minnesota Coalition for a Smoke-Free Society 2000, Minneapolis, Minnesota, March 14, 1985.

26. Quoted in Marc Kaufman, "Surgeon General Favors Tobacco Ban," *The Washington Post*, June 4, 2003, https://www.washingtonpost.com/archive/politics/2003/06/04/surgeon-general-favors-tobacco-ban/c0e64edd-df67-486b-86d5-31bad58abf2a/.

27. Christopher Snowdon, *Velvet Glove, Iron Fist*, (North Yorkshire: Little Dice, 2009), 64.

28. Associated Press, "Carmona Joining E-Cigarette Board," March 24, 2013.

29. Warner, "An Endgame for Tobacco?".

CONCLUSION

1. James P. Carse, *Finite and Infinite Games*, (New York: Free Press, 1986), 37.

2. David Courtwright, *Forces of Habit*, (Cambridge: Harvard University Press, 2001), 206.

3. Philip Morris International, "Designing a Smoke-Free Future," accessed June 1, 2019, https://www.pmi.com/who-we-are/designing-a-smoke-free-future.

4. Daniel Kolitz, "Meet the Activist Leading the Lonely 'Smokers' Rights' Movement," *Hopes and Fears*, undated, http://www.hopesandfears.com/hopes/now/politics/216869-smokers-rights-activist.

5. Christopher Buckley, *Thank You for Smoking*, (New York: Random House, 1994).

6. Nell Zink, *Nicotine*, (New York: HarperCollins, 2016), 59.

7. Gregor Hens, *Nicotine*, trans. Jen Calleja, (New York: Other Press, 2015), 1-2.

8. Richard Klein, *Cigarettes Are Sublime*, (Durham: Duke University Press, 1993), 6.

9. Klein, *Cigarettes Are Sublime*, xi.

10. Klein, *Cigarettes Are Sublime*, 17-18.

11. Klein, *Cigarettes Are Sublime*, 3.

ACKNOWLEDGEMENTS

1. Laia Jufresa, *Umami*, trans. Sophie Hughes, (London: OneWorld Publications, 2016), 121.

INDEX

CPSIA information can be obtained
at www.ICGtesting.com
Printed in the USA
LVHW091029071019
633397LV00006B/194/P